KU-326-281

FROM PILCHER TO THE PLANETS

Percy Sinclair Pilcher, flying his 'Bat' Mark 3 glider at Auchensail near Cardross, Dunbartonshire in 1895
His first successful flights were in the interim 'Bat' sometime in June/July 1895
He was 'Assistant Lecturer to the Naval Architecture and Marine Engineering Class at Glasgow University from November 1891 to April 1896
and Draftsman in the shipbuilding firm of J & G Thomson, Clydebank', (which became John Brown's)
Pilcher designed and built four gliders during 1895/96 – 'Bat', 'Beetle', 'Gull' and 'Hawk'
The latter did not fly in Scotland but was successfully flown at Eynsford in Kent
He had his fatal accident on his third flight of the afternoon of Saturday 30 September 1899 at Stanford Hall, near Rugby
having been due to fly his new and intended to be powered triplane, that day – the UK's first flying fatality, aged 32
The illustation is based on one of the first photographs of a man in flight depicting Pilcher at Auchensail
where on 12 September 1895 it is recorded that he flew for 20 seconds at a height of 12 feet

FROM PILCHER TO THE PLANETS

FROM PILCHER TO THE PLANETS

*Aspects of Glasgow and
the West of Scotland's early
contribution to aviation as seen
against the history of flight and
a view of the art of engineering*

Dugald Cameron OBE DSc

Roderick Galbraith D Univ

Douglas Thomson

Published by the University of Glasgow 2003

The views expressed are the authors' alone.
Any surplus from this publication will be devoted to
the Royal Air Force Benevolent Fund.

The historic University of Glasgow where Percy Pilcher,
Britain's first aviator taught, is home to
the only Department of Aerospace Engineering in Scotland –
educating aerospace engineers and conducting
internationally renowned programmes of research.

In all its spheres of activity, the Department
seeks to broaden its base even further by extending
its working partnerships with universities, institutes and industry
throughout the world.

Published by the University of Glasgow 2003

Copyright   The Authors

All rights reserved.
No part of this publication may be reproduced
stored in a retrieval system or transmitted in any form or by any means
electronic, mechanical, photocopying, recording or otherwise
without prior permission in writing from the publisher.

ISBN: 0 85216 778 X

Designed by James W Murray
Historical illustrations by Dugald Cameron
Illustrations scanned and retouched by Alan Carlaw
Printed and bound by The Bath Press

CONTENTS

Dr Richard Green in the small low speed closed return wind tunnel during an experiment unique to Glasgow

Sir George Cayley's triplane glider of 1849 in which a 'boy was wondrously floated above the earth'
2003 sees the sesqui-centennial of his 1853 'Coachman' flight

INTRODUCTION

Lord Selkirk of Douglas PC QC MSP
(Lord James Douglas-Hamilton)

SCOTLAND has made an early, effective and remarkable contribution to aviation, enabling enormously improved travel and communications.

The authors have told in a colourful and authoritative account the significance played by some inventors, pilots and pioneers at a time when heavier-than-air flight involved tremendous risks to life and limb.

In the early 20th century, aviation was a new idea and the visionary statement by Sir George Cayley, as early as 1815, caught something of the spirit of the pioneers: [The air was] 'an uninterrupted navigable ocean that comes to the threshold of everyman's door.' Clearly he believed that every opportunity should be taken to advance the prospects of aviation in the best interests of mankind.

The Scots have always been in the lead of inventing and have been responsible for almost one-quarter of Britain's greatest inventions, and the authors cover the significant extent of the Scottish involvement in being at the forefront of the cutting edge of new technology. But the individuals who were the first to test the new aircraft, when it was only just technically possible, were confronting the perils of the unknown.

When Neil Armstrong used the phrase 'a small step for man – a giant leap for mankind', he was echoing the views of every pioneer who sought to advance the possibilities of flight. As I write these words I am conscious of the reality that if the first flight over Mount Everest had encountered even greater difficulties, my father and David McIntyre would not have survived, and I would not be writing this introduction.

The pilots could not have operated without the engineers, and Sir David Henderson, Frank Barnwell and James and William Weir all made a tremendous difference, with their strategic view. As a result, the men and women who played a key role in creating the Royal Air Force, the Royal Auxiliary Air Force, and the Women's Royal Air Force can rightly be proud of their tremendous achievements.

This book honours the participants and tells in great detail the story of how aviation developed in Scotland, and it comes at a particularly relevant time as there is a risk that, with controlling interests of multi-national companies existing outside Britain, the important jobs being undertaken by Scots in this field may not necessarily receive the recognition which they deserve.

It is to be hoped that by highlighting the sure and steadfast services of Scots men and women, this book will enhance the prospects for employment, education and enterprise, with a view to invention and innovation for the benefit of everyone.

A debt of gratitude is owed to the authors for their skill in bringing forward to a much wider audience some of the trials, tribulations and triumphs which have catapulted Scots to fame on the ground as well as into high places in the air.

Everyone who has an interest in Scotland's heritage will be grateful to have access to the information in this highly entertaining, well-written account.

Clyde Built! Queen Elizabeth II and Jetstream 31

FROM PILCHER TO THE PLANETS

Aspects of Glasgow and the West of Scotland's early contribution to aviation as seen against the history of flight and a view of the art of engineering

Dugald Cameron

IF THE 19th CENTURY can be described as the age of steam then the 20th can claim the conquest of the air. The impact and influence of aviation and its many technological spin-offs have shaped much of those turbulent times, for good and ill. The development of flying has enabled the peoples of the world to see its wonders, each other, and enjoy their diverse cultures. A great industry has been created, together with the enormous expansion of world trade – but it has also brought a new dimension to warfare out of which arose the the Royal Air Force. At first, some even imagined that the coming of the aircraft would eliminate war. Sadly, such optimism was misplaced!

Science and even technology are neutral in terms of good and evil. It is for us, as human beings, to determine how best to use our creativity to maintain and advance the cause of civilised life on our planet – or not.

At the centenary of the Wright brothers' pioneering, powered, heavier-than-air flights of 17 December 1903, it is worth recording and recognising Scotland's, and in particular Glasgow's, early contribution to the remarkable first century of practical aviation.

Against the historical backdrop of the story of flight, and an occasional journey down some of the associated highways and byways, this essay looks at aspects of some of the work of two people in particular: Lieutenant General Sir David Henderson in the founding of the Royal Air Force, and Frank S Barnwell in designing and building (with his brother Harold), the earliest successful, all- Scottish, powered aeroplane. Others who made significant contributions to the early development of aviation

such as Bertram Dickson and the Weir brothers, William D and James G, are included in an attempt to paint the broader picture. Brothers feature notably in the history of early aviation.

What truly constitutes success in powered heavier-than-air flight is, in my view, that a machine carrying a pilot (that is someone with the means to determine the conduct of the flight) can take off under its own power (assuming that there is a source of lift), fly under control and land on a point at least as high as that where it began. An understanding of *lift*, *stability* and *control*, together with the availability of a suitable source of power was necessary for successful flight. In this, the achievments of Wilbur and Orville Wright stand supreme, as evidenced by the careful and systematic approach contained in their written records. Therein lie the keys to the Wrights' success. In May 1899 Wilbur Wright wrote to the Smithsonian with regard to flight and seeking all the information which they could give him: 'I am about to begin a systematic study of the subject in preparation for practical work'. They alone understood that the determination of a means of three-axis control and the availability of a power plant which could supply sufficient power while being light in weight (ie having a high power to weight ratio) were essential for successful manned, powered, controlled and sustained flight. This they successfully provided. Using these parameters, the many early attempts at flight (including ground runs which, on encountering a bump, threw the craft into the air momentarily, a not uncommon occurrence) can be excluded. What the Wrights did might be used as the practical test of other claims. Those early pioneers had not only

The 'First Flight' by the Wright brothers on 17 December 1903, 10.35 am Eastern Standard Time at Kitty Hawk, North Carolina, USA
Orville flying, Wilbur running behind

to invent their aircraft but also, having done so, learn to fly it on their first flight – designer, aerodynamicist, builder and test pilot in one!

Samuel Pierpoint Langley, Secretary of Washington's Smithsonian Institution attempted to fly his full-size 'Aerodrome' from a houseboat on the Potomac just before the Wrights' successes at the end of December 1903. He failed and from that failure arose a dispute between the Wrights and the Institution over priority which was only resolved in 1948 just before Orville's death.

It was the ongoing, passionate defence of their patents, from 1906, which may have contributed to Wilbur's early death. '– A short life full of consequences,' his father wrote in his diary. The inscription on the Wright brothers' memorial at Kitty Hawk, North Carolina says it all:

'In Commemoration of the Conquest of the Air by Wilbur and Orville Wright. Conceived by Genius, Achieved by Dauntless Resolution and Unconquerable Faith.'

It does seem such a pity that the Wrights took to litigation and allowed it to take them over, diverting them from creating the great business which should surely have been theirs. Did they invent the aviation lawyer? Though Orville lived until 1948, and went on to develop other inventions, he had sold his interest in the Wright Company by 1915.

The earliest sentient beings must have envied birds their freedom to move in space. Thus was born the desire, the determination that we should emulate them and fly. Kites – the most rudimentary of aerofoils – have been used from around 1000 BC and sails before them. How to make a sail, in effect an aerofoil, and harness the energy of the winds was known to some of the earliest people – the first known illustration of a windmill dates from around 1290 – but the idea of turning it through 90 degrees to make a wing does not seem to have occurred. It took Sir George Cayley in the early 19th century to use the kite form as a wing, though Leonardo da Vinci had got very near to a workable glider.

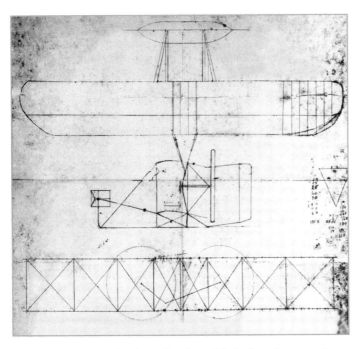

The plans for the Wright Flyer 1 that the Wright brothers drew on a piece of brown wrapping paper

It seems to me that the principal practical steps towards the achievement of sustained, heavier-than-air, powered and controlled flight were:

Pre-history – practical flying machines progressed from kites, (including man-lifting types), the oldest form of flying machine, invented by the ancient Chinese around 1000 BC. They were used for fun and then for military purposes from about 200 BC. The Chinese also, in 1100 AD, developed rockets. It seems however that the Chinese ruling class placed the proper administration of their Empire higher in their scheme of things than science and technology, which might explain their failure to develop the kite into a practical flying machine as we would recognise it. *Plus ca change*!

The earliest practical 'aircraft' were models, thus unmanned.

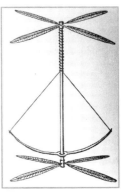

How it began–a child's toy (a string pulled helicopter) c. 1325 and Launoy and Bienvenue's model of 1784

As we celebrate the centenary of powered flight, sophisticated 'uninhabited' air vehicles – UAVs – are being widely developed for military purposes both reconnaissance and offensive. Is the wheel coming full circle?

The first recorded ideas about flying from a British scientist are those of Roger Bacon in 1250.

The earliest man-lifting 'powered' machine would seem to be a child's toy – a string-pulled helicopter device illustrated in a Flemish manuscript of around 1325. Versions of this kept appearing including that of Launoy and Bienvenue in 1784 – one year after the first aerial voyages by balloons in France.

The time will come when thou shalt lift thine eyes
To watch a long-drawn battle in the skies,
While aged peasants, too amazed for words,
Stare at the flying fleets of wondrous birds.
England, so long mistress of the sea,
Where winds and waves confess her sovereignty,
Her ancient triumphs yet on high shall bear,
And reign, the sovereign of the conquered air.

1737 – from Thomas Gray's *Luna Habitabilis*

1783   first aerial voyage – by Francois Pilatre de Rozier and the

Marquis D'Arlandes in a hot-air balloon from the Chateau de la Muette, in the Bois de Boulogne, Paris on 21 November.

1784   on 27 August James Tytler made the first ascent into the air by balloon in Great Britain, at Comely Bank, Edinburgh.

1785   Blanchard and Jeffries made the first crossing of the English Channel by air in a hot air balloon on 7 January.

1799   Sir George Cayley, inventor of the aeroplane, inscribed a silver disc with the basic configura tion of an aircraft as we know it.

1803   The world's first practical steam-powered *ship* was the 'Charlotte Dundas' a stern wheeled paddler designed and built by William Symington and tried on the Forth and Clyde Canal in March, just before Trevithick's locomotives.

1809   Cayley's full-size glider.

1849   Cayley's boy-carrying glider flight at Brompton Dale, Yorkshire.

1853   Cayley's 'coachman carrier' at Brompton Dale.

1857   Frenchman Felix du Temple made a bold but unsuccessful attempt to fly with first a model, then a full-size steam-powered machine. His model was however the first such powered craft to leave the ground.

1876   Nicholas Otto built the first practical high-compression engine, having defined the four-stroke cycle and devised a means for ignition. Karl Benz produced the first motor car in 1885 and Percy Pilcher, with his partner Wilson, began making small engines during the 1890s. The Wrights designed and built their own 12 hp engine for the 1903 aircraft.

1890   Frenchman Clement Ader managed a hop or so with his 'Eole' in 1890 and 1897.

1891   Otto and Gustav Lillienthal begin flying their 'hang' gliders near Berlin.

1895   Percy Pilcher (born Bath,1867) continued the work begun by Otto Lillienthal, successfully flying his gliders at Cardross on the banks of the Clyde. Pilcher, a former apprentice at the Randolph Elder (Fairfield) Shipbuilding Company on the Clyde, was assistant to John Biles, Professor of Naval Architecture at the University of Glasgow.

1903   The Wright Brothers, Wilbur (born Millville, Indiana 1867, same year as Pilcher, and Orville (born Dayton, Ohio 1871) made the first true powered and sustained heavier-than-air-flights at Kitty Hawk, North Carolina USA on 17 December at 1035 Eastern Standard Time. Well might we celebrate their genius, their careful methodology and their courage, one hundred years later. They too had started with a toy!

1905   The Wrights demonstrated the world's first real practical aircraft at Dayton, Ohio, with three- axis control and capable of prolonged flight.

1906   First powered flight in Europe by Alberto Santos-Dumont, 23 October, Paris.

1909   Louis Bleriot makes the first crossing by aeroplane of the English Channel, marking the resurgence of European aviation.

When reflecting upon the sterling efforts of our own pioneers it is as well to bear in mind the achievements of others. The Wrights were demonstrating a real practical aircraft in 1905, which could fly distances and manoeuvre under control in the

James Tytler, baloonist
Edinburgh 1746

air, and Bleriot showed his mastery in 1909 – but it is a matter of record that the first ascent into the air by balloon in Great Britain was that of James Tytler 1784 in Edinburgh and that the first heavier-than-air flights were those of Percy Sinclair Pilcher during July 1895, at Cardross on the Clyde.

The purpose of this essay is to accord due recognition to Scotland's particular place and priority in the quest for flight, set against its general history, and to recognise the crucial role played by Scots in the development of military aviation: in particular, the creation of the Royal Flying Corps and the Royal Air Force.

Today, the only military flying units based in the West of Scotland, where about half of Scotland's population live, are the search and rescue Gannet SAR Flight of the Royal Navy at Prestwick, and the Universities of Glasgow and Strathclyde Air Squadron who fly from Glasgow International Airport, with their town headquarters in the west end of the city. They carry on a great tradition and perform a vital role in creating air-mindedness among tomorrow's leaders, supplying well-trained and motivated graduates for the Royal Air Force while maintaining its operational presence in this part of Scotland.

A number of distinguished senior officers, and many who have made their mark in civilian life, can be counted in the ranks of the squadron's alumni. Sir Thomas Risk, former Governor of the Bank of Scotland was in the first (1941) intake and went on to fly Sunderlands during the War, and others include Lieutenant General David Huddleston, a law graduate of 1959, who enrolled in the Royal Canadian Air Force and retired as Commander, Air Command in 1993. Though before

the Squadron's time and in aviation medicine, Air Vice-Marshal W K Stewart (1913-1967), a science graduate of 1934, and medicine in 1936, made significant contributions in that field, including research (using himself as a guinea pig!) into the factors which determine the onset of blackout in aircrew, improved oxygen systems and the effects of sudden accelerations and decelerations. The latter was of great value in aircraft catapult and ejection seat design. He was head of the RAF Institute of Aviation Medicine from 1947 until his death.

From the earliest times, there were many individuals with ambitions to emulate the birds, a few of whom built weird and wonderful contraptions in order, they hoped, to do so. We know of some, but others keep surfacing, attracting enthusiastic champions to their cause. In all such cases the questions: what is the evidence? where is the corroboration? should be asked, for without satisfactory answers such claims only exist because people want to believe in them. Rarely however, are the main established facts of the story of flight seriously challenged, in particular, the Wright brothers' priority.

In 1993 I had the pleasure of hearing from a former member of the Royal Flying Corps about the early days. Major James Morton, a pilot who served from 1916 to 1918 and who was then in the excellent Erskine Hospital for ex-servicemen and women near Glasgow, revealed that his 'flying instruction' amounted to three-quarters of an hour, beginning by sitting behind the pilot on a Farman biplane! Such though is practical aviation's recency that I regularly meet a lady who told me a few months ago that she had served in the Royal Flying Corps, which she quickly corrected to the Women's Auxiliary Army Corps, in 1917 at the experimental seaplane base at Loch Doon. As I write in the spring of 2003, Miss Grant should soon celebrate her 107th birthday!

That a sustainable Scottish aircraft industry was eventually created, after very early but short- lived ventures, followed by

D F McIntyre and the Marquess of Douglas and Clydesdale

much more extensive attempts by Beardmore during and after the First World War, was due to the vision and determination of David Fowler McIntyre, born in Glasgow on 24 January 1905, and associated with Govan, like Arthur Whitten Brown (of Atlantic crossing fame 1919). He learnt to fly at the Beardmore Reserve Flying School at Renfrew, joined and eventually commanded 602 Squadron, and became co-conqueror by air of Mount Everest in 1933 and co-creator of Prestwick Airport, Scottish Aviation Ltd in 1935 and Scottish Airlines – all in collaboration with the then Marquess of Douglas and Clydesdale, future 14th Duke of Hamilton. The Duke, Scotland's premier peer, was to give great personal support to SAL during the difficult financial times in the 1950s. SAL is now, via British Aerospace Ltd, BAE SYSTEMS and is still in the aircraft designing and making – ie 'aerostructures' – business at Prestwick though once again as a subcontractor. As this is being written

there are no complete aircraft at BAE SYSTEMS Prestwick and the aerostructure business is up for sale (2003) as it is not 'core business'. This seems to be a fashionable concept these days but one might wonder if those who talk thus know where they are really going. This company now has, in the wake of the government's relaxation of ownership regulations, (and like Rolls-Royce), a majority of its shares in foreign hands. Is this another of our once great industries being sold down the river, at the behest of the 'City' (of London)? Is this an opportunity for one of the few Scottish businesses of international stature to take over a skilled workforce and a creative engineering capability?

David McIntyre was influenced by the great visionary statement of the father of aeronautics, Sir George Cayley in 1815: [The air was] 'an uninterrupted navigable ocean that comes to the threshold of everyman's door ought not to be neglected as a source of human gratification and advantage.' This quotation served to inspire McIntyre, as did the Earl of Selkirk's choice of motto for Scottish Aviation Ltd – from Robert Burns', '*A Man's a Man for A' That*'– 'The World O' er'. What McIntyre and Clydesdale did they did out of a sense of duty, not for personal gain. In these days we might well reflect on this. David McIntyre had seen the effects of economic depression on the Clyde and was determined to create a new industry to counter the decline of shipbuilding.

Prestwick Airport itself, much expanded and developed during the Second World War, is, in 2002, experiencing something of a renaissance greatly assisted by the growth of the 'no frills' carrier Ryanair and the significant expansion of freight traffic. Indeed, the area around the airport is being developed as an 'airpark', using its great natural advantages.

Ironically, these were the men who had selected Abbotsinch as the new base for 602 Squadron in 1932, thus being responsible for both of the West of Scotland's future airports! The future may show just how wise they were. Tragically, David McIntyre was killed in one of his own aircraft, a Twin Pioneer, which suffered a structural failure over Libya in 1957 during a sales tour.

It has been said that 'David McIntyre's major achievement was to realise his vision and build a substantial aviation industry here which is thriving more than sixty years on, and to have created the basis for a modern airport which gave international status to Prestwick and its community and performed an invaluable role in the Second World War'. His son, Dougal, is a graduate in aeronautical engineering from the University of Glasgow.

In 2002, aerospace is worth about £2 billion annually to the Scottish economy, employing 15,000 people directly plus 7,000 indirectly. The UK aerospace turnover at the time of writing (2002) is over £18 billion – 55% is civil, 45% military, a 50% growth over the last ten years. It employs nearly 150,000 directly and 350,000 indirectly and is a high value, high tech, high skilled, high wage business with 33% of its employees holding degrees or their equivalent. That can be seen against the Boeing company's turnover in commercial aircraft alone of about £23 billion in 2001 and a total for its aviation activities of around £38 billion.

On 11th June 2003 BAE SYSTEMS Aerostructures at Prestwick delivered its first wing assembly to the Airbus assembly facility at Broughton in North Wales. This is described as this plant's first such design and build contract.

Just as well that Tony Benn's decision to renounce the ambitious European Airbus plan in 1969 was overcome by the then Hawker Siddeley group–now BAE SYSTEMS. The crassest ministerial decision in British aviation history according to the late Handel Davies then Deputy Controller of Aircraft in Whitehall.

So after a century of powered flight there is but one significant complete aircraft made in the UK, the 'Hawk'originally designed by Hawker Siddeley in the 1970s but much developed and still going strong!

The economic importance of our airports is demonstrated by the University of Strathclyde's Fraser of Allander Institute's recent study, showing that in 2001 the British Airports' Authority's Glasgow Airport contributed £709 million to the Scottish economy.

The airship the R 34 at Inchinnan.
It completed the first return crossing of the Atlantic in July 1919

The story of Rolls-Royce in Scotland from its beginning here in an Air Ministry 'shadow factory' at Hillington in 1940, to the present times is worth an account of its own. As this is being written, the decision has been taken to relocate their original Hillington plant to a new facility at Inchinnan, thankfully still in the West of Scotland, thus maintaining an indigenous high technology manufacturing capability and capacity, and in a nice historical coincidence, where Beardmore test flew both 'heavy' bombers during 1918 and the transatlantic airship, R.34, in 1919. Sadly, Rolls-Royce's Scottish aero-engine design department was closed in 1996. Some of its staff formed East Kilbride Engineering Services which, in 2002, was employing 120 people in both aero-engine and general engineering design together with manufacturing and recruitment consultancy.

Rolls-Royce's facility at East Kilbride, established in 1953 for the production of Avon engines, is, in 2002, enjoying a renaissance in the internationally competitive jet engine maintenance and overhaul business.

Ferranti, over at Turnhouse, had a proud record of design and development in avionics and is now a part of BAE SYSTEMS, having previously been taken over by Marconi, and we should not forget some of the others whose names are no longer current such as the King Aircraft Corporation, established at Hopeton Place, Glasgow during 1941, and subsequently at Hillington. Others have taken their places such as GE Caledonian (established as Caledonian Airmotive), in engine overhaul, Woodward in engine nacelles and Polar Air in aircraft overhaul and maintenance all at Prestwick, particularly their own 747 freighters. Their first 'C' check on a 747 was due in early 2003.

Loganair, 'Scotland's airline', is once again independent under Scott Grier's able chairmanship. Through it, we retain links with the earliest days of commercial aviation in the UK, let alone Scotland, for the routes it currently serves to the Highlands and Islands and to Orkney and Shetland are among those pioneered in 1933/34 by John Sword, E E Fresson and Eric Gandar Dower from Glasgow (Renfrew), Inverness and Aberdeen.

Loganair was established by Duncan Logan, the contractor, in 1962 and Captain 'Mac', Duncan McIntosh.

John Sword's Midland and Scottish Air Ferries pioneered the Scottish Air Ambulance Service in 1933 at Renfrew. Many noted aviators would become involved with it such as Captains David Barclay MBE and Eric Starling, both of whom served with British European Airways before the service was taken over by Loganair in 1973. 2003 sees the 70th anniversary of their Glasgow to Campbeltown service, the first scheduled air route in Scotland.

It is worth noting that the first 'humanitarian' flight was the delivery of urgently needed medical supplies to Islay on 1 August 1930 by Griffith Powell and David Lloyd in an Avro 504N of 602 (City of Glasgow) Squadron) Auxiliary Air Force, from Renfrew – the first Auxiliary Air Force Squadron to be formed. The first Royal Naval Volunteer Reserve to be established was the 'Clyde Division', in October 1903. The Scottish Air Division was formed in 1947.

Mention should also be made of two other great Scottish aviation institutions, the Scottish Aero Club, at Scone, one of whose constituents was the Scottish Flying Club, formed in 1927 by a group of ex-Royal Flying Corps and Royal Naval Air Service veterans at Renfrew. They went on to become the biggest such organisation in the UK and became the managers of Glasgow's Renfrew airport. Ten years later, the Scottish Gliding Union was established and, like the Scottish Aero Club, it is flourishing at its Portmoak base beside Bishop Hill on the shores of Loch Leven.

The City of Glasgow's educational establishments have also played their part in the development of aerospace for over a century, in particular the University of Glasgow and the University of Strathclyde and its antecedents. With their sister institutions, they might well be regarded as the cradles from which the new science and technology sprang. As perhaps the city's largest employer now, higher and further education is well placed to maintain this vital role in the future.

Samuel Johnson, the great lexicographer, was moved to record, in 1759 *"'If all men were virtuous", (returned the artist) "I should with great alacrity teach them to fly. But what would be the security of the good if the bad could at pleasure invade them from the sky Against an army sailing through the clouds neither walls, nor mountains, nor seas, could afford any security. A flight of northern savages might hover in the wind, and light at once with irresistible violence upon the capital of a fruitful region that was rolling under them"'*. A remarkable and cautionary tale for the future from that querulous lexicographer and writer, many years before even the first balloon flights. Other literary figures were to be equally perceptive

'Oh, for the wings of a dove', wrote the psalmist, yearning to emulate the birds and fly. Many were the attempts so to do, but the story of mankind's conquest of the air is the stuff of myth and legend, from Icarus, whose overweening ambition led to

The bombing raid by a Lancaster in which it's pilot Bill Reid won the VC and the attack on a U-Boat by a Catalina in which its pilot John Cruikshank won the VC. Bill Reid and John Cruikshank in front of a Catalina. John Cruikshank's crew, left, and a photograph of his attack, right. In itself a rare record

disaster, to countless jumpers, flappers and floaters. The flight of birds however is far more complex than the 'flappers' thought and attempts to copy them were wholly unsuccessful!

The 20th century saw mankind's dreams realised and aviation became one of its greatest triumphs and defining achievements. The invention and development of the aeroplane has truly changed and transformed our world, for good and for ill.

Some parts of this narrative were written in the immediate aftermath of the terrible terrorist attacks on the USA on 11 September 2001. The wings of doves were turned into the talons of hawks by the inhuman and perverted minds of evil men, and became the means of mass murder and destruction. The world moved into new and terrible times. An awful shadow fell over

the pursuit of flight and the whole aviation industry went into retrenchment, a process begun before the events of 11 September but exacerbated and deepened by them. But the peaceful purposes of aviation which have done so much to bring people and peoples together, enhancing and expanding their lives, will surely triumph over the forces of evil.

Justice is a necessary condition for peace though what that is to adversaries in conflict is usually far from being easily determined or settled to their mutual satisfaction. War may be both necessary and just, as was the case in the Second World War. It has been a dreadful but constant companion throughout human history. It deals out death, and causes destruction and degradation throughout which there are also great acts of individual and collective gallantry, by ordinary people placed in extraordinary circumstances, such as those which were recognised and rewarded by this country's highest honour for valour, the Victoria Cross. Of the six Scots airmen who were awarded this medal during the Second World War, three survived the conflict and two were with us until recently, John Cruickshank and Bill Reid. Bill graduated BSc in Agriculture from the University of Glasgow in 1949: sadly, he died on 28 November 2001. Let us also salute Kenneth Campbell, John Hannah, Hugh Malcolm and George Thompson. Real heroes for all time.

Dan Ferguson's drawing of John Damian's leap

John Damian, leaping off the battlements of Stirling Castle during 1507, was Scotland's first flyer, unsuccessful though he was in his attempt! James (Balloon) Tytler took up the challenge of the air, ascending from Comely Bank in his Edinburgh Fire Balloon, on Friday, 27 August 1784, a year after the world's first aerial voyage – that of the Marquis D'Arlandes and Francois Pilâtre de Rozier in their hot air balloon. They ascended from the Chateau de la Muette, in the Bois de Boulogne, Paris, on 21 November 1783 in a Montgolfier balloon. The first real Scottish aerial voyage was by Lunardi on 5 October 1785 from Heriot's Hospital, Edinburgh to Ceres in Fife. His balloons inspired the 'Lunardi' bonnet as quoted by Burns in *To a Louse*, written that year. Early days of jumpers and floaters! One attempt from Paris resulted in their balloon being torn apart when it landed at the village of Gonesse, where, in a tragic coincidence in July 2001, a Concorde crashed.

Lighter-than-air machines were the first means of aerial adventure followed by craft which could be steered, 'dirigables'. The French were prominent in these early experiments as they were to be in the development of heavier-than-air machines, hence the widespread use of French in aviation terminology. 'Flappers' were taken with the idea of mechanically replicating what they thought of as the method by which birds flew. Leonardo da Vinci, from around 1493 in Renaissance Italy, was one of many who were captivated but somewhat bemused by the apparent flapping action of birds' wings. Ornithropters have been a recurring, if as yet hopeless, theme in flying history. Poor imitation of bird flight rather than an understanding of it has been the pattern over the years. Leonardo devoted much time and effort to the question of flight: however, it was not until the 19th century that his work resurfaced by which time it had been overtaken, though his ideas for a glider and a helicopter were of significance. 'To be an artist during the Italian Renaissance was to be an engineer'.

At the (two-year-old), Aeronautical Society of Great Britain's exhibition of 1868 in the Crystal Palace, a Glaswegian engineer, Joseph M Kaufman displayed a model quadruplane ornithropter which was demonstrated to destruction using its steam engine. Might Kaufman be Glasgow's first aeronautical adventurer, showing his machine in the year of Charles Rennie Mackintosh's birth?

Tytler was, however, Britain's first aeronaut for he beat Lunardi, in England, by a few weeks – Lunardi's first ascent being the month after Tytler on 15 September 1784, while James Sadler, the English balloonist, made flights during that October. Tytler's pioneering efforts (although perhaps not too successful) in Scotland, and his prority in the UK, would seem to have been unfairly suppressed, despite ballooning, or 'aerostation', becoming all the rage.

The first scientist to have ideas about flying was Roger Bacon in 1250 but it was Sir George Cayley, that very remarkable English baronet from Brompton Hall, near Scarborough,

Sir George Cayley

who first understood how lift could be generated from a plane surface angled to the oncoming air. 'The whole problem is confined within these limits, to make a surface support a given weight by the application of power to the resistance of air.' He also suggested that a curved surface was likely to be more effective than a flat one. Horatio Phillips later on developed that into the double-curved section first used by the early experimenters. Cayley noticed that birds didn't drop out of the sky when they stopped flapping their wings from which he concluded that 'lift' and 'propulsion' had to be separated – he nevertheless persisted with the idea of flapping paddles in his 1849 and 1853 machines. He well understood that the use of steam engines was unlikely: however, in what aviation historian Charles H Gibbs-Smith calls 'The French Paper', a submission to J F Dupuis-Delcourt, (founder of the world's first aeronautical society), Cayley refers to 'Mr Stirling of Glasgow' with respect to the latter's developments in the more economical use of steam: (Rev. James Stirling, inventor of the Stirling [*steam*] engine).

On a silver disc, dated 1799, Sir George inscribed the basic form of what we can recognise as an aircraft and in 1804 he built and flew a model glider, the wing of which was a kite in form as was the 1852 published design. (It should be noted that the Wright brothers initially flew their first gliders as kites.) In 1809 he built a full size man-carrying craft which, it would seem, was launched into the air from sloping ground. Cayley's subsequent work led to the triplane glider of 1849 in which a 'boy was wondrously floated above the earth' – this was the first aircraft to be drawn/designed, built and flown. Regrettably, we do not know the identity of the boy passenger. *(see p. 6)*

In 1852 Cayley published his design for a 'governable parachute' – in fact an aircraft. The following year he built two multiplane gliders and his 'new flyer', in which his groom or coachman, possibly John Appleby, became a somewhat reluctant passenger – 'Sir George, I tender my notice, I was hired to drive not to fly'. Nonetheless he must be the first recorded person to experience heavier-than-air piloted flight. In 1947 a replica, based on the 1852 design, was constructed and flown over Brompton Dale by glider pilot Derek Pigott.

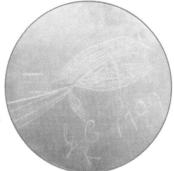

The silver disc dated 1799 with Sir George Cayley's inscribed basic form of an aircraft

Cayley understood the need for a suitable power source but was fixated on the idea of 'flappers', derived from his ornithological observations as a means of propulsion, useless in fact. His gunpowder engine, though not successful, did in some way anticipate internal combustion. The remarkable Baronet was over 75 years of age when he devised, built and conducted these epoch- making experiments, and this was very far from the sum of his achievments for he was active in many other spheres including proposals for an 'air engine'. He was also the founder of the Regent Street Polytechnic in 1838.

Wilbur Wright is quoted in 1909 saying – 'About 100 years ago an Englishman, Sir George Cayley, carried the science of flying to a point which it had never reached before and which it scarcely reached again during the last century.' No better testimony to Cayley could be offered than that. The Wrights' centenary is also the sesquincentenary of Sir George Cayley's coachman's flight.

With the customary benefit of hindsight it might be wondered why no one had made the connection between the way a sail provides lift and how, turned 90 degrees, it could become a wing and supply vertical lift, thus making elementary flight possible. What that ignores is that although practical sailing is ancient in origin, at least 3000 years old, an understanding of its principles as we now know them is not. It is surprising nonetheless that gliders were not experimented with before Cayley. He did influence John Stringfellow at Chard in Somerset who had made attempts at flight in model form around 1848, and later in 1868. In 1842/43 Stringfellow, with William Samuel Henson, had conceived a remarkable venture, the 'Aerial Transit Company' and even patented its 'aircraft' the 'Ariel' in 1842. This, though based on Cayley's ideas, pre-dated Cayley's 'Boy Carrier' of 1849 and must have influenced future experimenters here and on the continent. It only appeared in model form powered by one of Stringfellow's beautiful, light steam engines. It did not fly and the bold venture was abandoned. As with much of early aviation history, it has become the stuff of myth and legend.

- -

As the centenary of powered flight approaches, and with the various anniversaries which fell in 2001 related to the University of Glasgow and with its sister institution, the University of Strathclyde, it can be seen that the City of Glasgow's place – indeed, Scotland's place – in aviation's relatively short history is more significant than is generally appreciated.

- -

2001 – a year of anniversaries

- -

550th of the founding of the University of Glasgow in 1451, 44 years after John Damian's leap from Stirling Castle, Scotland's first recorded event in aviation history.

90th of the Barnwells' flight of 30 January 1911 at Stirling, the first, by an all-Scottish aeroplane of more than half a mile, winning them the Scottish Aeronautical Society's J R K Law Prize of £50.

60th, of the establishment of the University of Glasgow Air Squadron, now the Universities of Glasgow and Strathclyde Air Squadron.

50th, of the establishment of the Degree in Aeronautical Engineering at the University of Glasgow.

On 17 December 2003, at 10.35am Eastern Standard Time, we will celebrate the centenary of Orville and Wilbur Wright's four epic flights at Kitty Hawk, North Carolina, USA – the first manned, heavier-than-air, powered, sustained and controlled flights in human history. The first that day, flown by Orville, lasted 12 seconds and covered 120 feet; the fourth, flown by Wilbur, 59 seconds and 852 feet, was really the most significant.

- -

Percy Pilcher, assistant to Professor (later, Sir) John Biles, and lecturer in Naval Architecture at the University of Glasgow from 1891 to 1896, was Britain's first true fixed-wing aviator. He was also Britain's first aviation fatality. His achievement is commemorated in the name of an annual lecture given in the University of Glasgow.

Excerpts from *To Percy Pilcher*

Youthful dreams of flight, nurtured in your heart,
Matured as you matured; became a part
Of ev'ry waking day.
And pensive hours on land lost, windswept seas,
Where graceful, long-winged seabirds soared with ease,
Helped guide you on your way.

How great a game of chance, how close to fame,
Yet few are those who now recall your name
or what your courage meant.
The lonely grave in Brompton where you lie
grows mossy underneath a mocking sky:
A short life bravely spent.

But those who now traverse the lofty ways
in these jet-powered, ocean-spanning days
Cast hist'ry in their wake.
You knew this time would come, and played your part
In teaching Man a new and wond'rous art:
And gave life for its sake.

Philip Jarrett, 19 April 1983

Percy Pilcher's Hawk, built in Glasgow but never flown in Scotland

Percy Pilcher's sister Ella and a helper with the Hawk

Engineering education in Pilcher's time, at its highest levels, embraced a blend of the theoretical (university) and the practical (industry) for both students and staff. Percy spent his summers as a draughtsman in the shipyard of J & G Thomson, Clydebank, (subsequently John Brown & Co.). In my view it is a pity that the necessary growth in the syllabi for engineering and the contraction in the number of firms has diminished the importance of this partnership in academic programs. Engineering is a practical art and it is in industry that it finds its real expression. This may be recognised but it has yet to be fully accepted by all concerned. Pilcher's boss, Professor John Biles came from industry and continued a distinguished professional practice while holding his Chair – typical of the time though I guess it is not usual now. That great engineer Professor J MacQuorn Rankine, managed so well to combine theoretical understanding and investigation with practical endeavour and the writing of poetry, not to mention Professors Barr and Stroud, founders of the great, eponymous Glaswegian scientific

Sir David Henderson   *Frank Barnwell*

enterprise which still remains, under French ownership. What would today's Funding Councils say and could the Research Assessment Exercise cope?!

Professor J McQuorn Rankine proposed the idea of shock wave ('shocks') in 1870.

Two other notable 'Glaswegian' aviators were featured in the Pilcher Memorial lecture of 2001: Lieutenant General Sir David Henderson, the most important infuence in the creation of the Royal Air Force, and undoubtedly the founder of its predecessor, the Royal Flying Corps, together with pioneer designer and flier, Frank Barnwell of Balfron. We must also remember the latter's brother and first partner in aviation, Harold; and the highly politically influential and effective organiser, in the formation of the third service, William Douglas Weir, subsequently Sir, Lord, and finally, the first Viscount Weir of Eastwood. His brother, James G Weir, was a very early Scottish flyer who went on to

further the development of the autogyro and from that develop the helicopter – work continued to this day in the research undertaken at the University of Glasgow by the Department of Aerospace Engineering. The Department's story, so far, will be related separately here by Professor Roderick Galbraith together with Dr Douglas Thomson, its current Head.

'Where does history begin What wealth of interesting material has been destroyed by selfish, thoughtless, uninterested and ignorant men For example, take the broken fragments of Pilcher's glider, seen once in a cupboard by my father in the University of Glasgow. He was lectur-ing in Aeronautics, and went later to look for it but a janitor or cleaner had thrown it out for firewood He himself had built a glider when he was in his teens. I still have a length of bamboo pole, part of the frame-work, seen in a photograph taken in the Home Park, near the site of his windmill.'

This comes from Dr Archie Thom's biography of his father Professor Alexander Thom, published in 1995. It makes sad reading – the more so since we in the City of Glasgow haven't yet learned to value what we once made, and it's not the jan-nies' or cleaners' fault!

Sadly in this centenary year, the first development Jetstream 41 aircraft, the last commercial aircraft to be designed and built in Scotland, has been refused a place in our Museum of Flight, alongside that of its predecessor, the prototype 31. Our care for our manufacturing heritage – what ordinary people have made – leaves much to be desired. Future generations will wonder at our carelessness.

The definitive account of the origins of air power and its development and use during the First World War by the Royal Flying Corps and, latterly, the Royal Air Force, is that of Professors Sir Walter Raleigh and H A Jones in their multi-vol-ume, the official history, *The War in the Air.* Raleigh became the first Professor of English Literature at the University of Glasgow in 1900, before being appointed Oxford's first such professor of that subject in 1904. Among his friends in Glasgow was the architect Charles Rennie Mackintosh. He was knighted in 1911 and died on 13 May 1922 after contracting typhoid fever while the aeroplane taking him to the Middle East was marooned for four or five days in the desert between Jerusalem and Baghdad. He had been preparing the second volume of his account and was returned to England where he passed away at the Acland Home, Oxford. His first volume was published soon after. There is a memorial window to him in the library of Merton College by R Anning Bell, sometime Head of Design at Glasgow School of Art.

In his preface to the first volume (his only one) he says, 'Some of the men who early took thought for their country's need and quietly laboured to prepare her against the day of trial are here celebrated, and their names, we hope, rescued from neglect.' This is typical of Raleigh's careful, decent and thorough approach to his task.

Why was a professor of English literature commissioned to write the first historical account of air warfare? Raleigh was much exercised by the war and began writing and speaking about issues which it raised in an Oxford Pamphlet *Might is Right*, 1914. His addresses, *The War of Ideas*, December 1916; *Some Gains of War*, February 1918 and *The War and the Press*, March 1918, together with *The Faith of England* March 1917 and his British Academy lecture *Shakespeare and England*, 1918, were published in a volume *England at War* in July 1918. It is therefore not too surprising that, given his academic eminence and evident impartiality, he was commissioned to do the job. His text is beautifully composed and most carefully considered. The final work of six volumes plus two of maps and a set of appendices is a seminal account, the bulk of which fell to Professor H A Jones to complete.

Charles H Gibbs-Smith quotes Raleigh in an apposite and typically heartfelt comment on the flying corps experience: '*The air service still flourishes; its health depends on a secret elixir of immortality, which enables a body to repair its severest losses. The name of this elixir is tradition, and the greatest of all achievements of the air service is that in a very few years, under the hammer of war, it has fashioned and welded its tradition, and made it sure. Critics who speak of what they have not felt and do not know have sometimes blamed the air service because, being young, it has not the decorum of age. The Latin poet said that it is decorous to die for one's country; in that decorum of age the air service is perfectly instructed.*' Would that we might heed such wise words.

The aeroplane certainly, and obviously, changed the conduct of warfare, but how decisive was the aeroplane in that terrible conflict? What cannot be doubted was the great sacrifice of its airmen. It was during the First World War that fighting aeroplanes began to be developed and that aircraft design and technology began its road to maturity.

The City of Glasgow was at its zenith as the 19th century gave way to the 20th. Its splendid City Chambers still proclaims that suberb civic confidence, energy and ambition which must have imbued its leading citizens, leaders in so many spheres of human endeavour. Its industries and commerce, from a strong local base, had conquered world markets by their great inventiveness and entrepreneurial energy, assisted by the marketplace provided by the Empire. They were well placed to face the new century. Japan came to the Clyde to learn from us. Might we not now ask them back to show us how to build ships effectively and efficiently? Charles Rennie Mackintosh himself was inspired by aspects of Japanese art and design, brought over by trade.

Glasgow designed and built steam locomotives for our railways and the railways of the world, with another McIntosh, John Farquarson, at St Rollox, introducing his beautiful and powerful 'Dunalastair' 4-4-0 steam locomotives for the Caledonian Railway – around the time when Charles Rennie Mackintosh was creating the new Glasgow School of Art and Pilcher was flying at Cardross.

From the Clyde went great ships, built on its banks, to all the oceans, taking with them its many and myriad manufactures to

Truly Clyde built! *Fairfield's* EMPRESS OF SCOTLAND

customers around the globe. The British Empire, for so long as it lasted, provided us with a huge captive market. The great art of engineering, so well expressed by the Victorians, was all around to see and to employ. Truly an art for everyone and by everyone, whether it be a ship, a locomotive, the machinery for sugar refining, or the bringing of pure water from Loch Katrine to Glasgow. Such was their success that much that the Victorian engineers created is still in use, even if rather neglected over the years, a back-handed tribute to their practical skills and organisation.

Such is our present failure, that by taking it all for granted, and having been lulled into a false sense of economic or industrial security in the aftermath of the two world wars, we failed to emulate their ambitious and audacious vision and take it forward. We could still do so if we really wanted to for the intellectual and practical skills are still there – political vision, will and above all leadership of a high order are desperately needed though!

I might be accused of expressing a rose-tinted view of these

earlier times and conveniently glossing over the harsh and crude workplace conditions then faced by ordinary people, and the fear and poverty which characterised the lives of so many of the working class. I know enough from my own father's recollections of his time in the yards, as an apprentice in John Brown's, Clydebank, and subsequently as a journeyman, to be under no illusions as to the hard and uncertain nature of early 20th century working life. He was laid off when work on the Queen Mary was suspended in 1931, and journeyed south to find employment at the Ford plant at Dagenham, there to experience the treadmill of the production line. Happily, he was invited back by his former foreman in the yard when work recommenced on the '534' in 1934.

Just after I was born, at the outbreak of the Second World War, he moved over to the new 'shadow' factory built for Rolls-Royce at Hillington to produce the marvellous 'Merlin' aero engine of Spitfire, Hurricane and Lancaster fame. His wages doubled overnight and he worked with a roof over his head, even with heating, and they gave him a micrometer rather than a ruler with which to measure! The change in circumstances allowed me to attend the High School of Glasgow and begin to see a wider world. My mother, a Yorkshire lady, was determined that I would not go into the yards. They had, by her careful management of my father's shipyard wage, bought their own house in Yoker, and then given me my opportunity. It was not that popular a move in the family, even though education, the 'democratic intellect' of the Scots, has been well recognised as the key to the door of social progress. As I write, my father now in his 100th year, has been a pensioner of that great firm Rolls-Royce for longer than he worked for them and must be one of their oldest. Let me record our gratitude to them.

The rapidity of development in aviation has been such that my father, born just before the Wrights' epic success in 1903, has seen the practical realisation of flying, the coming of the jet-age and, in 1969, the year after he retired from Rolls-Royce, the first man on the moon – all well within a normal human life span, let alone an extended one. Only 66 years separate Orville's and Wilbur's footsteps on the sands of Kitty Hawk from Neil Armstrong's and Buzz Aldrin's footsteps on the dust of the moon.

The lunar landings led to the space shuttle with its reusable vehicles and extensive scientific experiments and a manned space station. The first mission was that of 'Columbia' on 9 April 1981 – Brunel's birthday. Tragically two of the Shuttles have ended in disaster – Challenger' on 28 January 1986 just after take-off and 'Columbia' herself just before landing on 1 February 2003. This programme is witness to the USA's overall leadership in aerospace and to the continuing courage and commitment of the men and women who fly these demanding missions.

from *Pilot Magazine* May 2003

After more than thirty years during which it has travelled 7,600,000,000 miles, it seems that the Pioneer10 spacecraft which once explored Jupiter has sent its last, very weak signal to Earth.

Dr Colleen Hartman director of NASA's Solar System Exploration Division said."Pioneer 10 was a pioneer in the true sense of the word. After it passed Mars on its long journey into deep space, it was venturing into places where nothing built by humanity had ever gone before. It ranks among the most historic as well as the most scientifically rich exploration missions ever undertaken."

Pioneer 10 carries a gold plaque that describes what humans look like, where we are and the date when its mission began. Rather like the Marie Celeste, Pioneer 10 will now continue to fly as a ghost ship through deep space and on into interstellar space. It is heading in the general direction of the red star Aldeberan, about 68 light years away, but it won't reach there for another 2,000,000 years or so. NASA has no plans to attempt any further contact with Pioneer 10.

Will Mars be the next objective? Professor Colin McInnes' solar sails might give the answer.

1969 was something of an *annus mirabilis aeronautica*. As well as the moon landing, the Boeing 747 'Jumbo' made its maiden flight ushering in the era of mass, cheap air transportation, and the Anglo-French Concorde flew, allowing supersonic air travel – for a few. Its economics, perhaps, did not eventually match its superlative concept and design and it was dogged by ill-intentioned politicking, scaremongering by self-styled environmentalists and, more significantly, the huge rises in the price of Middle East oil. Perhaps if our American friends had been successful in their attempts at designing a supersonic transport aircraft, Concorde would have fared much better and supersonic travel would have become more widespread and acceptable politically. The industry had thought that supersonic transport would be the way forward for passengers and that the 747 would be for freight, hence the latter's inspired design with a clear deck and cockpit perched on top. It was not to be and the 747 is still selling and a huge success.

Other Scots involved in Concorde were Sir James Hamilton from Penicuik who worked at the Royal Aircraft Establishment, Farnborough, on wing design and later became Director General Concorde, Ministry of Technology. Bob McKinlay, Engineering Development Officer and John Cochrane, Test Pilot.

What timing for the centenary year of powered flight – British Airways and Air France announce the cessation of supersonic air travel with the withdrawal from service of Concorde due to adverse trading conditions. The end of the first commercial supersonic age will come on 31 October 2003, not quite 100 years after the Wrights' epoch-making flights on 17 December 2003. There will be a successor, surely, one which will carry more people and at hypersonic speeds, for speed is the nature of air travel.

'Never has such a beautiful object been designed and built by man. The aircraft is not going to stop because it continues to live in the human imagination.'

Jean-Cyril Spinetta, President of Air France

August 1968, the year before the moon landing, saw the last regular steam haulage on British railways, after a glorious, if at times arduous, 140 odd years. Sir George Cayley (1773-1857), the father of aeronautics, had begun his work on flying around 1799, just before the first steam railway locomotive by Trevithick in 1804, the year in which Cayley began flying his model gliders. The first moveable steam engine was that of William Murdock of Cumnock's model steam carriage of 1794. Murdock was to join Watt (and Boulton) in Birmingham though it is said that Watt was initially reluctant to employ him as he was of the view that Scots didn't make good engineers!

The steam age and the beginning of real aviation might have begun around the same time but steam power, all that was then available and remaining so until the coming of the internal combustion engine, could never have been a practical means of power for flight given the weights of machine and fuel, even for Stringfellow's very light constructions.

The North British Locomotive Company, founded in 1903, designed and built 11,500 locomotives for railways worldwide by the time it closed in 1962.

Perhaps what can be said about what was made by ordinary working people is that, despite some of the conditions in which they lived and worked, there was a pride and satisfaction in the job. Was that, and the kind of camaraderie there was in the yards, the antidote to a working life of toil and struggle? It is not difficult for me, in comfort and with hindsight, to wax romantically about what was created on the Clyde and its hinterland, yet I feel a sense of anger and betrayal at the way that manufac-

Class YP locomotive (India State Railways)
is hoisted on board ship at Stobcross Quay, Glasgow

turing, especially shipbuilding, has been so carelessly thrown away, particularly as the new 'sunrise industries' are collapsing all around and world shipbuilding continues unabated.

After the Second World War management and men between them, through economic myopia and a general unawareness, along with misplaced, political ideology, comprehensively lost the plot and threw away almost the whole Clyde shipbuilding industry, and, indeed others – needlessly in my view. Neither nationalisation, nor the subsequent reprivatisation necessary for any kind of survival, provided a means to maintain shipbuilding at anything like its former importance though happily, in 2001, there are still ships being built in three yards on the Clyde – BAE SYSTEMS at Govan and Scotstoun and further down the river at Frank Dunnet's Ferguson yard, Port Glasgow. Nationalisation of UK shipbuilding in the mid 1970s proved to be a disaster, introducing a precursor to what I have described as 'managerialism' in the form of 'managers' seriously inexperienced in that particular business. Had we brought in Swedes or

Japanese or Germans, maybe the results would have been better and perhaps sustainable. That an island nation has so mismanaged its political/commercial/industrial affairs that it no longer has a substantial indigenous commercial shipbuilding industry nor, in fact, an indigenous commercial aircraft manufacturing capability, should be a matter of great concern. Silly talk of 'sunset industries' cannot disguise this shameful situation.

How is it that the new 'Oriana' could be recently built at Papenburg, 40 kms down the Ems river in Germany with all their European labour and social costs, and the new 'Queen Mary 2' is being built in France? We must surely wonder at the scale and scope of our misjudgements in political, economic and industrial strategy during the last fifty or so years and should be truly ashamed!

Yet, yet, yet we were told by all those smart and clever people on the sidelines, that the heavy industries, such as shipbuilding on the Clyde were finished and the future lay in the service sector such as in these desperate call centres, or the brave new world of electronics, providing we could bribe those international companies to locate in Scotland and show us how to do it.

There seems at times to be a regrettable reluctance on the part of our civic authorities to celebrate the 'industrial art' that their forebears produced, as if they are slightly ashamed of it, while happily spending what depleted resources they now have on the 'fine' arts for Glasgow's undoubtedly splendid municipal galleries. Glasgow's much loved and used Transport Museum needs to be greatly increased in scope and show much more of our people's products, while there are still some left. Where are the representatives of the thousands of locomotives built at Springburn for the world? They are a fast dwindling number and it ought to be a priority to repatriate one or two while we can. They would act as a reminder and inspiration for the future.

Culture is a distillation of what we all produce, not just an elite. Glasgow's culture in particular arises, or maybe more accurately, arose, out of its industrially created wealth – what we made. The city was justly given due recognition in 1990 as 'European City of Culture', for the home it gives to the national music, opera, and ballet companies not to mention its beloved Citizens' Theatre and the prominence of so many of its artists, old and new. Its splendid architectural heritage, widely recognised and even appreciated now, was so much dependent upon, and sustained by, the city's erstwhile industrial, mercantile and commercial success. What was designed and made, and exported to the world was, in its own way, an art form, though largely unrecognised as such then. It contributed hugely to the great human art of engineering. We badly need to renew our capability in this field and we can do it. The seeds are being well sown in our universities and in our School of Art, itself originally established 'to assist local manufacturers in the design of their products'. This should be a matter for our reconvened Parliament if it has the mind to do so.

That much grander concept, 'civilisation', owes its existence to communities managing to produce a surplus of wealth thus allowing them to indulge in non-essential, ie non-survival-related activities. Art, life enhancing and illuminating as it can be, is maybe something of an indulgence! Perhaps it does not change much though artists, by reflecting what they see, can moderate society and can be useful critics. Art at its best, however, is life sustaining. Perhaps we need to reintroduce the concept of artists as artisans and bring back the skills which were once their prerogative.

A country's true identity is made manifest by its accumulated culture, in the widest sense, and must include that which its people make, not just the products of its artistic community.

In our universities, and higher and further education institutions, depressed as they have been during the last twenty years or so by the growing menace of managerialism and lack of investment, lie the seeds of our future.

The vital need is to educate for making it and doing it, rather than talking about it or writing about it, a credible view given

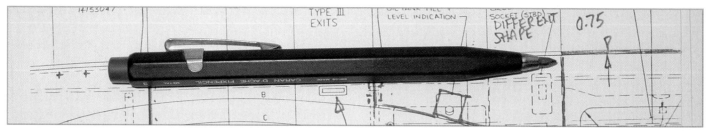

the parlous state of so much of our national infrastructure, and the increasing public contempt for politics, as witness the poor turnout at elections. Design, the process which creates real products, still seems to lie in the uncomfortable but exciting no-mans-land between art and science, begging a proper understanding in the face of conventional wisdom. Charles Gibb, writing in the *Scottish Review* No. 79, puts it well – "Received wisdom is when information goes into somebody's head and comes out again without having been subject to any thought processes. Thus, for example, it is widely believed that environmentalists are always right'. Global businesses now exercise more influence, even more power, than properly elected governments, with the latter being content to huddle together in 'communities', wallowing in a debilitating and, eventually, self-defeating bureaucracy and buttressed by useless over regulation. Much of this seems to be more about political vanity than human progress.

Engineering is often easier to depict than to describe. One striking thing about engineers – apart from their disenchantment with the managerial class set above them and the trivialised culture which neglects them – is how often they want to draw things, words not being up to the work of describing technical reality. 'Give us a pen,' engineers would say, 'look, it works like this' .

Engineering is a great art and one in which we all participate in some way or another. It is very demanding of those who take on its challenges but immensely satisfying at its peak – an amalgam of beauty and utility.

Yes, drawing is the true language of the designer in all fields – the basic tool of creation – the means by which designers talk to themselves and then show to others their ideas, and it can still be achieved quite satisfactorily using that most wonderful of inventions, the humble lead pencil!

If we really believe in the necessity of a healthy manufacturing economy – and heaven help us if we think that call centres and the like can replace it – then it is what is made, the product, that must lie at its heart, and the process that creates the product is called 'design'. It is the creative, practical process of design which begins the business. Smart production engineering and proper marketing, however, must be an integral part of the whole process of putting products onto the shelves but, without an inspired product concept, the rest will be either difficult or unsuccessful. Style, as opposed to substance, is not design in its fullest or proper sense, though it is, at its best, a legitimate component of the whole. Making junk or unwanted products efficiently is, if anything, even more useless than doing it badly, as you get much more of them.

Has the UK learned any lessons from its woeful experience of manufacturing decline during the last fifty or so years? Judging by our recent efforts to produce new railway rolling stock, once one of our great industries – indeed one we invented – the answer appears to be a resounding NO. It seems to me a particular nonsense that the 'service' sector is being touted as where all our futures should lie when as a nation we seem to be ill-equipped and unsuited to the business of providing service. We are unable to differentiate between service and servility in the way that others do and take pleasure from doing. Our poor record in tourism is proof of that. The current fashion for 'call centres' is a case in point, for not only do they often fail to deliver real service but what the poorer ones do seem to provide is poor service and an inhuman workplace.

Every age can seem to have been a 'Golden Age' in retrospect to some, and hindsight has always 20/20 vision, yet we *did* manage these affairs so much better even in the 1930s, as witness in 1935, the LNER's ability to conceive, plan, design, build and successfully introduce into service their high speed train, the 'Silver Jubilee', within seven months, yes, seven months! This without the benefit of computer-aided design and the other sophisticated techniques of today, and at a time of considerable financial stringency for the LNER company. Thank you, Sir Nigel Gresley, where are your successors?

Current red tape and regulation, with too many levels and too much government – Europe, UK, Holyrood and local. Why are there so few engineers in our Parliaments yet so many lawyers – referees of life rather than players?

In service industries and in education, staff morale is what determines success – far, far more than the unthinking application of management theory, and that requires informed, experienced direct leadership truly in touch with all those involved in delivering the service.

There is no one more pathetic than he (or she) who aims low and misses. George Scott-Moncrieff

Scotland might not make the most of anything but it can, in well chosen fields, as Ivor Tiefenbrun's Linn Products has demonstrated, make the very best, and sell it to the world.

Henry Royce, that greatest of our engineers, had the artist Eric Gill carve over his fireplace the Latin aphorism – *Quidvis recte factum, quamvis humile praeclarum.* "Whatever is rightly done however humble, is noble". It is an inspiring and truly inclusive proposition for it applies to everyone and whatever they do.

The 19th century might be characterised by the development and application of the power of steam to which this University's James Watt made such a notable early contribution and to Glasgow's great Professor J MacQuorn Rankine, who provided such a fundamental understanding of the science involved. Both the development of steam power and its exploitation on rail and on the first steps toward the conquest of the air might well be regarded as part of our great Victorian legacy, though the railway quite rapidly achieved almost its full potential before the end of the 19th century, while aviation had still to become a practical reality.

The coming of railways, made possible the change from horse to steam power, and brought a revolution in internal transportation, creating a greater UK market, and an enormous increase in manufacturing capability and capacity – the introduction of what we now know as mass production. It is sad to witness the decline in our railway system that has happened over the last fifty or so years and the disaster so needlessly brought about by their privatisation or, perhaps, by the particular way in which it was done. That the world's fourth largest economy can no longer manage its railways, a system it created and gave to the world and, worse, no longer has the capability to design, make and market the range of railway equipment it once did, employing the talents and industry of its people in so doing, is a tragic disgrace. What has happened since this fundamentally flawed privatisation was predicted by many inside and outside the railway industry. How, as a manufacturing nation – just – we have managed to survive the combined efforts of HM Treasury and the City of London is a matter of wonder!

Some of the signs presently coming from the aviation industry, taken with aspects of our own actual performance in the field, might suggest that aviation could follow in the footsteps of the railway industry. We have the talent to design and engineer world-class products but not, it would seem, the political will or management ability to do so.

Such a set-up brings with it a grisly army of 'management consultants', and sundry other camp followers. as was well summed-up by Peter Clarke writing in his column in *Scotland on Sunday* in response to an invitation to spend £600 listening to one of those itinerant transatlantic self-styled 'gurus', 'The ability to speak nonsense with an air of authority combined with 'real world experience' is an increasingly important business asset. It comes with non-stop executive gobbledegook of the highest calibre.' I trust he was engaging in serious irony. Naturally, 'political correctness', industrial strength, usually features too!

Decline in numbers of applications to study civil engineering at British universities, 1994-1999: 40%; growth in the number of Britain's lawyers: 400%.

Enough said!

As has been said the 20th century was, in many important ways, shaped by the conquest of the air and its consequences. It brought about an enormous expansion in international trade and created today's global marketplace, now accelerated by information technology. (Railways did that nationally in the 19th century.) It also brought about a revolution in the conduct of war.

Beginning with the continuing experiments of the very early pioneers, followed by the enthusiasts and the entrepreneurs, then by the professionals and the businessmen, it has become a mature, international industry. Though typically characterised initially by official reluctance and disinterest, potential military purposes and the spur of war acted as the main early agents of progress in flying. Here too the horse gave way to the machine, even, eventually in the cavalry, though not without a fight! Aptitude for flying was, quite reasonably, related to horsemanship for selection purposes.

Throughout, Glaswegians played a significant part in the development of aviation, including quite a few connected with this University and the University of Strathclyde. A number of its academics played important roles as government advisers in the early days, during the Second World War and after.

In many ways engineering and manufacturing is this city's birthright. Why are we now so shy at celebrating the achievements of our people? These products were conceived, created, and constructed by ordinary working people led by a professional and mercantile class who saw active particpation in civic affairs to be a natural and welcome part of their life – rather than the purely ceremonial, charitable and social roles currently undertaken by such people.

It is the artisans' art and skills that we should be able to enjoy and learn from. It was their work and the wealth it created that bought the architecture we now revere and the pictures which fill our galleries. In many of these engineering products there is a real art, perhaps more readily accepted through the patina of age: yet I would contend that it is in the products of technology, that the 20th century has expressed its creativity most successfully, and profoundly. It is found in such exemplars as the heroic engineering which allows us to extract oil from the hostile North Sea, build the Channel Tunnel or create Concorde, that powerful, inspiring and popular icon of the 20th century – a truly wonderful amalgam of science and art. How satisfying then that the reconvening of the Scottish Parliament in Edinburgh on 1 July 1999 should be celebrated by a magnificent flypast of Concorde leading the Royal Air Force's display team, the 'Red Arrows' – nearly 100 years after Percy Pilcher's death. Though not on the horizon yet, its successors must surely come and take the tedium out of long-distance air travel.

The micro-chip, which we take for granted now, and whose embodiment in the computer has so profoundly changed our times will surely rank as a wonder of the world. This is all perhaps, incidental to this tale. It is intended, however, to set the scene against which events of nearly one hundred years ago are told.

Poets and artists at their best have always managed to see not only their own times more clearly than others but offer a vision of the future, unalloyed by the limitations of contemporary science or technology, yet, remarkably prescient. Andrew Scott, a Scottish labourer, published some verses in 1826 which included.

Wha kens perhaps yet but the warld shall see
Thae glorious days when folk shall learn to flee:
When, by the powers of steam, to onywhere,
Ships will be biggit that can sail i' the air
Wi'a as great ease as on the waters now
They sail, an carry heavy burdens too.

An excerpt from *Locksley Hall:*
For I dipt into the future, far as human eye could see,
Saw the Vision of the world, and all the wonder that would be:
Saw the heavens fill with commerce, argosies of magic sails,
Pilots of the purple twilight, dropping down with costly bales;
Heard the heavens fill with shouting, and there rain'd a ghastly dew
From the nations' airy navies grappling in the central blue;
Far along the world-wide whisper of the south wind rushing warm,
With the standards of the peoples plunging thro' the thunderstorm;
Till the war drum throbb'd no longer, and the battle flags were furl'd
In the Parliament of man, the Federation of the world.
There the commonsense of most shall hold a fretful realm in awe,
And the kindly earth shall slumber, lapt in universal law.

Alfred, Lord Tennyson 1842

What an astonishing prophecy, containing an uncannily accurate vision and the expression of democratic hopes for a better future, from a great Victorian poet. He was able to imagine what might be ahead more clearly than some of his scientific peers.

It was just after this poem was published that Henson and Stringfellow's design for the Aerial Steam Carriage, the 'Ariel', was patented, leading to their grandiose but abortive scheme for the 'Aerial Transit Company'. The design was remarkable but existed only in imaginative lithographic prints showing the aircraft over such locations as the Pyramids, and in model form. There were no suitable engines then available!

Sadly, in our own time, Hollywood predicted in a film scenario the terrible events of 11 September 2001. That has often been the role of the artist, and still should be, though I fear it is not, so far as the present offerings of the visual arts are concerned.

Great art has to be more, much more, than self-referential one-liners, too often expressed without any real skill. '50 cent ideas expressed in $10 words'. Well might we revisit and revalue the creative vision and practical talents of our Victorian ancestors! All art is at its outset 'conceptual', but has hitherto gone much, much further and been so much more satisfying and sustaining. Yet the fashionable art of its time visually reflects something of the society in which it occurs: thus contemporary fine art practice echoes the consumerist society and, in its disavowal of specific skills, is managerialist in essence.

'Good art should,' the critcs tell us, 'move us, make us view the world afresh, challenge our assumptions, and delight us'. Great art should possess the sustaining power to do that in a way that significantly matters and moves us. At any time there will be little that can do this and little that will survive.

Is it significant that a surprising number of the earliest 19th/20th century experimental would-be flyers were artists or art students – Delagrange, artist turned engineer; Henri Farman, art student to engineer; and Gabriel Voisin, student architect? It does suggest the central place of the imagination, maybe the visual imagination, in such enterprises, if not an appreciation of engineering or practical methodology which can be inhibiting!

Aerodynamics deals with the behaviour of air flowing round a body. It is part of the larger science of fluid dynamics. It provides a powerful theoretical basis for the practical business of designing useful aircraft.

The early would-be-flyers however proceeded almost wholly empirically as the basic mathematics, not conceived until the middle of the 19th century by Claude Navier and Sir George Stokes with the Navier-Stokes equations – simple non-linear partial differential equations – were not usable in their complete form.

$$\frac{\partial \mathbf{V}}{\partial t} + (\mathbf{V} \bullet \nabla)\mathbf{V} = -\frac{1}{\rho}\ \nabla p + v\nabla^2 \mathbf{V}$$
$$\nabla \bullet \mathbf{V} = 0$$

The Wright Brothers' 1901 Wind Tunnel

Newton had also done his bit long before, in his great laws of motion.

In his book *Aircraft Design* Daniel P Raymer says: 'We have come a long way since 1879 when the annual proceedings of the British Royal Aeronautical Society [sic] could say "Mathematics up to the present day has been quite useless to us in regard of flying"'.

It was the Wright brothers who, in their careful, methodical and scientific approach to understanding the problems of successful powered flight, established a practical basis for it. Their wind tunnel, built after the difficulties of the 1901 flights, might be regarded as the beginning of true technological advance. Their success inspired and paved the way for the pioneers of aerodynamic theory, Ludwig Prandtl in Germany and Frederick Lanchester in Britain.

Concorde's superb performance, indeed its very existence, owes much to one of Prandtl's pupils, Dietrich Kuchemann, who came to the Royal Aircraft Establishment at Farnborough after the Second World War: such was the rapidity of advance in aerodynamics in its first fifty years. Professor Bryan Richards of the University of Glasgow's Department of Aerospace Engineering worked with Kuchemann at Farnborough.

The power of the digital computer, the late 20th century's most significant invention, has allowed theoretical techniques and the work of Euler, Navier and Stokes to be put to practical use in aero-dynamics and fluid dynamics generally. They are the basis for today's Computational Fluid Dynamics – CFD – among the most potentially powerful of tools now available to designers and engineers.

So does theory still come after practice? Are the wind tunnel and its wooden models still a necessary and relevant tool as so well used by that great aerodynamicist Richard Whitcomb of area rule, supercritical airfoils and winglets?

'I have not the smallest molecule of faith in aerial navigation other than ballooning, or expectation of good results from any of the trials we hear of. So you will understand that I would not care to be a member of the Aeronautical Society.' So wrote Lord Kelvin, responding to an invitation in 1896 from Major B F S Baden-Powell, secretary of the Aeronautical Society Society of Great Britain. It is surprising that he could not see the likely transformation in the quest for practical flight that the internal combustion engine would provide against the previous necessary use of steam.

In this, Kelvin was fulfilling the prophecy of the Aeronautical Society of Great Britain in its Report on its Exhibition (1868): 'In taking this step for inviting public scrutiny, the Society was prepared to expect some of the ridicule that has ever been attached to this subject, by those that are apt to mistake sarcasm for sound argument, but this cannot influence the success or failure of a particular question in science.'

The life and soul of science is its practical applications.

Lord Kelvin

Kelvin, Professor of Natural Philosophy at the University of Glasgow, was unquestionably one of this country's greatest scientists and he demonstrated his discoveries by putting into prac-

The statue of Lord Kelvin in Kelvin Grove Park, Glasgow

that 'it was one of the sensations of my life'. Much of Kelvin's teasing of Pilcher was kindly meant. In fact, according to Percy's sister Ella, very much his partner in his aeronautical adventures and possibly the first woman to fly, 'Lord Kelvin used to send chaffing messages to Percy about flying, but he gave us the use of a very large room at the top of the University to work in when the University was closed' – this was, it is believed, in the old physics area. In response to Professor Biles' request for assistance on Pilcher's behalf, Kelvin told him that 'on no account would he help him, nor should I (Biles) as he would certainly break his neck'.

Pilcher chaired a meeting of the Aeronautical Society of Great Britain on 26 May 1899 at which Lawrence Hargrave, the Australian aviation pioneer, described his box-kite ideas. These influenced Pilcher in the design of his last aircraft, the powered triplane. (Among the subscribers to Pilcher's later proposals was Mervyn O'Gorman who succeeded Capper as superintendent of the Royal Aircraft Factory, Farnborough – he resigned in 1917 after the arguments over the industry's right to design aircraft.)

Unfortunately, Kelvin was right in predicting Pilcher's likely end for he was indeed to suffer fatal injuries in a crash. On Saturday, 30 September 1899 at Stanford Hall, near Rugby, he flew in his fourth glider, the 'Hawk', built at Glasgow but not flown in Scotland. At about 30 feet there was a structural failure and man and machine plunged to earth. Pilcher was badly injured and he died two days later. He was aged 32, the UK's first flying fatality. The possibility that he might have flown his powered tri-plane – what he had intended to fly on that fateful day – and become the first to fly a heavier-than-air craft, died with him. That prize went to the two inspired bicycle makers from Ohio, Orville and Wilbur Wright, four years later.

This poem, *Elegy*, possibly written by Pilcher's sister and collaborator, Ella, (since it is not in his handwriting) and pasted into his photograph album, is dated 11 October 1895, around the time when Percy had first tested and damaged his third aircraft, the 'Gull'. It gives an insight into Percy's whimsical ambition,

tical and, indeed, commercial effect the theories which he so brilliantly propounded. Yet even he could not really see or imagine what the future in the adventure of flying might be, despite his colleague Pilcher's relative success the previous year at Cardross. With Lord Rayleigh he had visited Sir Hiram Maxim in 1894 at Baldwyn's Park in Kent and 'flown' in Maxim's machine, in effect a test rig. He was not impressed, remarking that it was 'a kind of child's perambulator with a sunshade magnified eight times'. Rayleigh, however, is reported to have said

frustration and the climate of academic respectability and scepticism in which he and Ella were working:

Oh I would I were a seagull
Or bird of any kind,
(for whether owl or other fowl
I would not greatly mind);
I would quit this world plebeian,
I would scale the empyrean,
And the moon and sun I would soon outrun
And leave them far behind.

If I had but sturdy plumage I'd flee this slavish crowd;
With tit and wren, with hawk and hen
I'd course amid the cloud.
But it still, alas doth fail me,
For the sour fateshot assail me,
and with jealous eye they observe, and try
To slay my project proud.

For I built me stately pinions
Like snowy canopies,
To breast the breeze and top the trees
And wheel about the skies.
I spread each spotless feather,
– Ah me, the traitor weather –
For there came one puff; it was quite enough:
In wreck their beauty lies.

So with purple oaths assist me
My fury to assuage ,
For I cannot hope my tongue will cope
With the measure of my rage.
Since up here I must seem proper;
(If my sister swears, I stop her)
Yet my studied smile cloaks a depth of guile
That no Devil's plumb could gauge.

One cannot imagine the serious and systematically minded Wrights engaging in poetry and expressing their feelings in such a manner! They had carefully and extensively researched the subject prior to proceeding, reading all the available literature, in particular the work of the French-born American Octave Chanute, who had published his *Progress in Flying Machines* in 1894. Having done so, they went well beyond him though he was a continuing source of encouragement. They were also well aware of, and acknowledged, Lilienthal's achievements and those of Pilcher. Chanute's work certainly inspired Pilcher. He had also been in correspondence with the Australian pioneer Lawrence Hargrave in 1896 over the latter's interest in box kites and their development (originally proposed by F H Wenham) although this had no real influence on Pilcher for by the time Hargrave came to the UK, it was too late. Hargrave had been experimenting with heavier-than-air model aircraft since 1882.

The Wright brothers suceeded in achieving a system of control on their aircraft after disappointing results from their 1901 machine led them to review their data and construct a wind tunnel. They then conducted tests, the results of which paved the way for the 1902 glider and the successful 1903 'Flyer' which in turn led to the world's first real practical aircraft in 1905.

Around the same time as Pilcher was beginning his experiments, Frederick Lanchester in 1894, was working on the basic theory of fluid dynamics related to lift – following Newton, Bernoulli, Navier and Stokes, Kutta and Joukowski. He also built a rubber-powered model aircraft which he flew from his house. In this he had been preceded by the Frenchman Alphonse Penaud in 1871. These models were the harbingers of mechanical flight. Lanchester's contribution to early aeronautical science was significant and cannot be overlooked. 'Official science' was somewhat disparaging of his early work in aerodynamics, even patronising. However, by 1926 he had achieved proper recognition. An echo of Kelvin re Pilcher here perhaps. *Plus ca change encore*

The first pilot-operated heavier-than-air machine was Louis

Charles Letur's parachute-type glider of 1853/1854, and the first powered machine to leave the ground (just) was that of Felix du Temple in 1874. In 1881 the Russian Alex Mozhaiski patented his idea for a monoplane which he built and attempted to fly in 1884. Though he may have left the ground it would not seem to have truly flown. These were bold and courageous attempts and, like those that went before and those that would come after, they deserve our admiration though what was achieved was not flight as the Wrights were so convincingly to demonstrate. Inevitably, having to use steam power with its weight penalties however beautifully made, coupled to a rudimentary understanding of aerodynamics and little idea of control, success was unlikely for a full-sized piloted aircraft though it was achieved experimentally by the Besler brothers in 1934 at Oakland, California. They believed that they could provide a more efficient condenser and thus reduce the amount of water required. Steam has one advantage, it is wonderfully quiet!

The development of the internal combustion engine, and with it the automobile, was the most significant stage in the achievement of powered flight. The early enthusiasts were often motoring 'toffs' such as J T C Moore-Brabazon (Aero Club Certificate No1, March 1910) and the Hon. C S Rolls, whose enthusiasms progressed from ballooning to motoring and then to flying. 'Brab' is one of the great figures of British aviation though he learnt to fly in France. Rolls, younger son of Lord Llangattock, having met the 'mechanic' Henry Royce, son of an improvident miller in 1904, co-founded their great eponymous firm in 1906.

The magic of a name ... Rolls-Royce remains an enduring synonym and symbol for excellence. Royce's standards remain its inspiration to this day. Sadly, Charles Rolls was killed in a flying accident in 1910 at Bournemouth, flying a French-built Wright 'A' machine. The kind of partnership then typical, between toff and technician, says something of our erstwhile social order and gives a clue to the awkward nature and attitude to technological progress in Britain and, perhaps, the historically low place of engineering in British public esteem. In order to gain acceptance to Oxford to study engineering, Brabazon, reluctantly, was required, to cram in Greek! Maybe today's computer scientists would be better educated with a grounding in the humanities!

From enthusiastic experimentation to pioneering, through barnstorming to a developing professionalism and on to today's global business and commerce might be a synoptic description of the first century of flying. It was one of remarkably rapid progress.

In some of the more imaginative literature of the later 19th and early 20th century, there was much speculation about the possible conquest of the air and its likely value to the military, particularly with regard to serving Great Britain's considerable Imperial interests and this was long before that purpose became a means of maintaining the fledgling Royal Air Force's continuing independence after the First World War.

Rudyard Kipling provided a remarkable vision on the future development of aviation and air power in *With the Night Mail*, 1904, and *As Easy as ABC*, 1907. He was accurate in some ways in thinking that it would open up the world but sadly wrong in his idea that it would put war 'out of fashion'. Kipling was a supporter of the British Empire. Like some others among his contemporaries he could see that air power might be a means of more easily exercising effective contol over indigenous populations at its outposts – what Hugh Trenchard or Frederick Sykes (who were both to play influential roles in the creation of the RAF) before him were to realise, and the former to initiate just less than twenty years later. In short, Kipling proposed the view that he who 'controls the air controls the world' – extravagant perhaps, yet nevertheless an astonishing vision at the time.

The first successful, powered, controlled, heavier-than-air, aeroplane flight in the UK would seem to be 'Col' S F Cody's hop at Farnborough on 16 October 1908, in his British Army Aeroplane

No 1. Cody (or Cowdery, as was his real name, should not be confused with 'Buffalo Bill' Cody, though he evidently sought to be associated with him) had produced the UK's first airship, the 'Nulli Secundus' at Farnborough in 1907. Around the same time on, it is alleged, 8 June 1908, A V Roe may have achieved some success in his canard biplane, first at Brooklands and then, having been 'evicted', under the railway arches at the Lea Marshes where he built his first triplane. He certainly flew successfully on 23 July 1909, the first British citizen to do so, if tentatively, in a British aircraft on British soil. Louis Bleriot flew the Channel a few days later! The Texan 'Col' Cody participated in the *Daily Mail*'s Round Britain air race of 1911, appearing at the St James racecourse, Paisley, control point – but a few hundred yards from today's Glasgow International Airport. He had previously built man-lifting kites as a better way than balloons of providing a reconnaissance platform.

Early aviation is surrounded by many dubious claims as to who was 'first' etc. compounded by genuine errors in dates and lapses in memory giving rise to such stories as that of Dundee's Preston Watson, with various people claiming his priority over the Wrights. This is a story which seems destined to reappear on a regular basis though there is no hard evidence to support it. It was thoroughly investigated by that most reputable of aviation historians, the late Charles H Gibbs-Smith after an article in the 'Manchester Guardian' in 1953 inspired by Watson's brother James. In discussion, James accepted that Preston's 1903 machine was a glider, not a powered aircraft. Gibbs-Smith wrote his careful findings and analysis in his 'Brief Preliminary Notes…' of 1957, the year of James Watson's death. The 1903 machine was, it would seem, a glider inspired by the Wrights. The subsequent powered aircraft, using Preston's superimposed 'rocking' aerofoil for lateral control, dates from 1908/9, with three machines being built and flown at Errol. Though he did not beat the Wrights, he experimented with a quite different system of contol for his machine – a kind of top mounted moveable wing.

Preston Watson himself stated in an article in *Flight* magazine, 15 May 1914 that: 'The method of preserving lateral equilibrium invented by the Wright brothers has been slavishly followed, but this has probably been due to the fact that these gentlemen were the first to fly in a practical way'.

This surely should have settled the matter for clearly what he was seeking to do was provide an alternative to the Wright system of control after their success. Nonetheless the story that Preston Watson beat the Wrights keeps on returning. He does deserve credit as a Scottish aviation pioneer, carrying on from Pilcher and inventing a novel means of lateral control. This was not successful, however, and in reality no real improvement to the Wrights' wing warping. Preston Watson was nonetheless a brave tryer and deserves recognition for what he did rather than what he didn't. He served as a pilot in the Royal Naval Air Service and was killed in 1915.

The New Zealander Richard Pearse also crops up as a challenger: however, despite his many inventions, there seems to be no evidence that he did achieve powered, controlled and sustained flight in his machine around 1902/3. Again, he himself made no such claims.

The real significance of any pioneer is surely in how they influenced or furthered future developments. Pilcher's work was among that known to the Wrights. It was only a few months after Pilcher's death that Wilbur Wright began the quest which in a relatively short time brought success to Orville and himself.

In some of these cases there is a bit of 'spin-doctoring' by latter-day supporters of these pioneers/enthusiasts, if not by themselves, and attempts to bolster national or civic pride. It is human nature to believe what we want to believe but without hard evidence it isn't really history!

Another early Scottish enthusiast was George Louis Outram Davidson from Banchory – 'Fleein Geordie'. Studying bird flight from about 1880, but not understanding it, he was flying a model glider in that area during 1897. He produced a number of remarkable proposals, published as prospectuses in order to solicit funds for his imaginative commercial flying machines including his 'Air Car' and 'Gyropter'. Having spent some £15,000 on his ideas he called it a day around 1911. He and Pilcher had met and crossed swords at a lecture which Davidson gave to the Aeronautical Society of Great Britain in July 1898 entitled, 'The Flying Machine of the Future'. He can claim to have invented the ABC airline guide, among his visions for future air transport. A V Roe was his draughtsman for a period. As Philip Jarrett wrote in his 1976 article in *Aircraft Annual*, 'Full marks for trying'!

The Short brothers began constucting aeroplanes around 1908, the first to do so in Britain commercially.

The City of Glasgow had its first sight and demonstration of a flying machine at Pollok Park on 2, 3 and 4 June 1910. It was given by James Radley in a Bleriot monoplane.

Aviation, in its earliest forms, was something of a public spectacle and entertainment, as in the case of balloonists such as Tytler, in 1784, and at the first flying meetings such as at Lanark in 1910. The Lord Provost of Glasgow at the time, A McInnes Shaw, seemed keen to promote this new science and chaired the meeting called to organise the event in March that year. Parachuting from balloons had also been a spectator attraction, engaged in by both males and females.

In Scotland, bold attempts at flying were made c. 1909 – Preston Watson at Errol, the Gibsons, father and son, at Balerno and Baird, the blacksmith from Bute, whose Bleriot lookalike 'louped a bit' on the sands of Kilchattan Bay. But it was the Barnwell brothers, Frank and Harold, from Stirling, who truly succeeded in achieving the goal of controlled heavier-than air-flight in 1911, though they had been designing and building aircraft and trying to fly since 1905. Their contributions will be told later in this account.

Lieutenant John W Dunne, from the Balloon Factory at Farnborough, had also been experimenting during 1907 and 1908 with swept-wing tailless aircraft, unpowered and powered.

The trials of these machines took place at Glen Tilt near Blair Athol, in secrecy, away from prying eyes. Dunne was particularly interested in building inherently stable aircraft but his attempt at powered flight was unsuccessful and he turned his attention to speculations on the nature of time. His aircraft have an uncanny resemblance in plan form to the current B2 stealth bomber!

Military aviation – the official view from the top, the conventional wisdom of the time, 1910:

'*...a useless and expensive fad*' Chief of the Imperial General Staff

'*...the naval requirement for aircraft is two*' First Sea Lord's estimate

Fortunately, there were men lower down the military hierarchy who could see the future potential of the military uses of aircraft. Men such as Captains Bertram Dickson and J D B Fulton and Lieutenant Launcelot Gibbs of the Royal Field/Horse Artillery. Gibbs had worked with Dunne during the flying trials with his tailless 'inherently stable' aircraft at Blair Athol in 1907 making him, effectively, the first pilot from the military. Perhaps Louis Bleriot's epic Channel crossing of 1909 served to waken up some official minds. Mainland Britain might not remain quite so secure in the future. As a contemporary newspaper headline put it: '*Britain no longer isolated*'.

If there was little awareness of the potential military uses of aircraft among the ruling top brass, at least one of a previous generation did try to stimulate interest and express concern at the Army's lack of interest – the popular Lord Roberts wrote to General Nicholson, CIGS, expressing a critical view of the official disinterest and subsequently made his opinions public in the *Army and Navy Gazette* of 1911.

Also in that year, Captain Bertram Dickson wrote: '*In the case of a European war, both sides would be equipped with large corps of aeroplanes, each trying to obtain information from the other, and to hide*

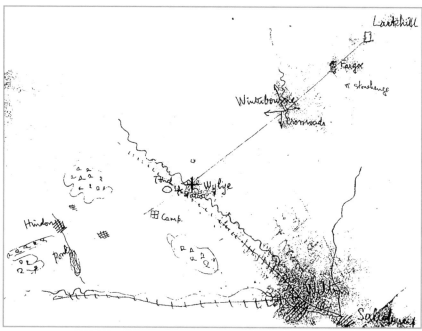

Captain Bertram Dickson June 1910. His sketch map of his flight across Salisbury Plain 21 September 1910 demonstrated the value of aerial surveillance

its own movements. The efforts which each would exert would lead to the inevitable result of a war in the air, for the supremacy of the air, by armed aeroplanes against each other. This fight for the supremacy of the air in future wars will be of the first and greatest importance'

Dickson was born in Edinburgh on 21 December 1873; his mother came from Ardrossan and his father from near Dumfries. He served in the second Boer War. Having had his offer to serve as a pilot rejected, he learnt to fly entirely at his own expense including buying, in 1909, his own aircraft, a Henri Farman. He learnt to fly at the Farman flying school near Chalons and was the first British officer to qualify as a pilot, getting his 'ticket', No.71, on 12 May 1910, just beating fellow Royal

Field Artillery officer, Captain J D B Fulton who would go on to play a significant role in the RFC.

Dickson must surely share in the credit for inspiring the eventual creation of the Royal Flying Corps and the Royal Air Force itself. He resigned from the Army on 3 August 1910 and proceeded to participate in the great Lanark aviation meeting a few days later, winning the aggregate, cross-country prize. This impressed Sir George White, of the Bristol Tramway Company, and enterprising founder of the British & Colonial Aeroplane Company, subsequently, the Bristol Aeroplane Company. He employed Dickson who was then invited with others to provide a flying demonstration to the Army during the autumn

BE 2s and a Maurice Farman of No. 2 Squadron, Royal Flying Corps at Upper Dysart Farm, Montrose, 1912. First operational military aerodrome in the UK

Frank Barnwell's Bristol Scout D of 43 Squadron Royal Flying Corps at Stirling, 1916

manoeuvres on Salisbury Plain in 1910. This was in his own machine, and at his own expense, at a time when officialdom, under pressure, was beginning to express some interest in aviation. The Army had invited a few pilots to participate, again at their own expense, as a way of 'keeping in touch' – no doubt as a means of keeping growing public opinion at bay. His 'reconnaissance' flight, in a Bristol Boxkite on 21 September 1910 is an event of great significance in the history of military flying. It is worth mentioning again that two intelligent, distinguished men, Haldane, in government, and Nicolson, Chief of the General Staff, were both then in the sceptical camp so far as the military use of aircraft was concerned, contained in a kind of mental prison, though with much less reason than Kelvin as steam power was no longer the only possible prime mover. The internal combustion engine had well and truly arrived!

Douglas Haig, then in India and yet to make his name and controversial reputation in the First World War, did then seem to show an interest in the developing military potential of the aeroplane. In May 1911 he wrote to the War Office seeking 'suggestions' on the matter, following demonstrations by the Bristol Company. Haig, it has been said, took an interest in technical developments unlike many of his contemporaries. He had indicated an interest in aviation while serving in India. Interest, however, did not lead to enthusiasm or understanding in the immediate future. That would come later but he would not, ever, become a supporter of a separate air force.

Among the more enlightened individuals of the early period were Colonels Templer and Capper, successively in command of the Balloon Factory; and Mervyn O'Gorman, subsequently in aircraft development at Farnborough, the birthplace of British military aviation. Capper had visited the Wrights as early on as 1904 and been impressed. Unfortunately, no deal was to be struck between them and the British government as they wanted $100,000 for a machine and another $100,000 for the design and know-how! The government wanted a demonstration first. Later on, the Short brothers (yet another set of flying brothers)

built Wright aircraft under licence, the first of which, in 1909, was for the Hon. C S Rolls. Official interest in aviation during the first decade of the twentieth century became centred on lighter-than-air airships rather than heavier-than-air aeroplanes.

While on a demonstration trip to Milan in 1910, Bertram Dickson was involved in the first ever mid-air collision on 28 September. The injuries he received were to shorten his life. He had been appointed in January 1911 by Sir George White as an adviser, while, significantly, continuing to lobby the government for the creation of a new air arm. He had become involved in the design of some of the early Bristol aircraft just before Frank Barnwell joined that company.

A few months after the establishment of the Air Battalion of the Royal Engineers in 1911, Dickson submitted a memorandum to the technical sub-committee of the Committee of Imperial Defence. This had been established by Prime Minister Herbert Asquith to enquire into the future of air power and included one David Henderson, then Director of Military Training at the War Office and his staff officer, Frederick Sykes, both destined to play significant roles in the development of air power and the Royal Air Force. In 1908, Henderson, having witnessed and appreciated the use of observation balloons while serving in the Sudan and during the Boer War, had become fascinated by press accounts of the epic flights of Wilbur Wright.

What was particularly significant about Dickson was his advocacy of the use of aircraft for offensive military purposes, rather than just reconnaissance; indeed, he foresaw the real future of military aviation with great clarity. He once remarked when questioned about personnel: 'One man is a rich man; another is an artist, or he is an actor; another is a mechanic. They are funny fellows.'

Sadly, on 28 September, 1913, Bertram Dickson died suddenly, from a stroke, at Lochrosque Castle, Achnasheen, Ross-shire. He was buried nearby at Achanalt, where a memorial was erected to him by the Highland Chapter of the Aircrew Association in 2000. He was truly a pioneer thinker so far as the use of air power as we have come to know it was concerned, and a progenitor of today's Royal Air Force. Almost certainly he must have influenced the thinking of the man who was to take the aeroplane to war, Sir David Henderson, and of course he and Frank Barnwell, as colleagues at the Bristol Company, must surely have met and discussed the future possibilities of aviation and the way forward in aircraft design.

From this era we should also remember Major Duncan Sayre MacInnes of the Royal Engineers. During the war, in 1916, he was employed under the Directorate of Military Aeronautics. 'Only those who worked with him will ever know how great a debt the Flying Corps owe to his industry and devotion.' Sadly, he too died early.

David Henderson, from a Glasgow shipping and engineering family, is regarded as the 'father of the Royal Flying Corps' and, given his memorandum of 1917 to Smuts, is surely the 'grandfather' of the Royal Air Force. Whether he met Frank Barnwell is a matter of conjecture. The world of flying was a very select band then! Subsequently, he was influential – perhaps the most influential individual, in making the case for a separate force.

Much of the necessary political support at this time came from William Weir, the Glaswegian engineer and industrialist, who had been recruited into government during 1915. Weir became Director of Munitions, Scotland, in July 1915; Controller of Aeronautical Supplies, Ministry of Munitions and member of the Air Board, February 1917; and Director General of Aircraft Production, December 1917. Being in agreement with the South African General Jan Christian Smuts' 1917 future air control and organisation proposals, initially as a member of the Air Board, and then as Secretary of State for Air, Weir was to be instrumental in bringing Trenchard back to the fold after the latter's resignation in April 1918 and, importantly, in fending off continuing attacks on the separate Service from the Royal Navy and the Army. This had been the subject of further consideration after the war: however the independence of the Royal Air Force was

William Douglas Weir
First Viscount Weir of Eastwood

confirmed. It would seem that the two Glaswegians, Henderson and Weir, did not get on as well as might be thought. The result of this we shall see later.

There was another Glaswegian connection in Andrew Bonar Law, born in Canada of Scottish extraction. He came to Glasgow to finish his education: first at the High School and then by taking classes in law at the university. He entered politics from the iron and steel business and became leader of the Conservative Party and co-premier in both the Asquith and Lloyd George wartime coalitions. After the 1922 general election – in which a number of 'Red Clydesiders' entered Parliament – the Conservatives returned to power and he became Prime Minister. (The High School had produced another Prime Minister Henry Campbell Bannerman.) Bonar Law is reported as taking the view in 1922, even after the matter had been settled, that the RAF should be disbanded and its units returned to their original services. His premiership was brief as he was in failing health. He resigned on 20 May, 1923 and died shortly afterwards. Whether he would have pursued his policy regarding the independence of the RAF can only be a matter for speculation. Trenchard was then well in control and even Admiral Beatty couldn't sink the new service! Thus, while two Glaswegians were instrumental in bringing about the new service, another was apparently of the view that it should be disbanded! Interestingly, Frederick Sykes, a future Chief of Staff and David Henderson's subordinate and rival, was to marry Bonar Law's daughter, Isabel.

Though Lord Weir had resigned from government soon after the end of the First World War, he remained an influential figure in air matters up to the outbreak of the Second World War, being an advocate of the Sykes – and indeed what became the Royal Air Force – doctrine of strategic bombing.

Subsequently Weir gave valuable support to jet propulsion pioneer Frank Whittle at a time when the establishment were uninterested in, or sceptical of, his proposals for the turbojet engine. He became President of the Scottish Flying Club, the leading and largest such organisation in the 1930s, with brother James G Weir its Chairman.

William Weir was a Clydeside industrialist of great ability brought into government service after the outbreak of the war. His talents as an organiser ensured his rapid promotion and he became a confidant of all the principal political leaders and, given his responsibilities for armament production and aeronautical supplies, he also got to know many of the key military personalities. His shrewd intellect readily weighed them all up. It was the job of the Ministry of Munitions to organise the effective and efficient production of the weapons of war, using the country's available industrial capacity.

He was a tough labour negotiator and did not seek to indulge the workforce. By far the best tribute to him is that his firm, 'Weir's of Cathcart' is not only still in existence, but is an international player with its corporate headquarters still where it was founded well over one hundred years ago. His great public service, though, continued in many other ways, such as in the organisation of the supply of electricity through the creation of the National Grid. He was also much involved in the re-equipping of the Royal Air Force in the years immediately prior to the outbreak of the Second World War. W J Reader's biography of him is well entitled *Architect of Air Power*. It was fitting that he was created first Viscount Weir of Eastwood in June 1938 and had the Honorary Degree of LLD conferred upon him by the University of Glasgow.

He died in 1959 at Eastwood and is remembered at the annu-al Dinner of the Universities of Glasgow and Strathclyde Air Squadron, through the Weir Trophy awarded to the best first year student of the Squadron, quite a few of whom have gone on to success in civil and military aviation.

The Weir company, particularly through James Weir, became seriously involved first in autogyro and then in helicopter development during the 1930s. David Kay of Perth had experimented successfully with autogyros from 1927, His second model is exhibited in the Museum of Flight at East fortune alongside the later Weir W2.

Among the first attempts to make and fly a helicopter however must surely be that of the Denny/Mumford machine(s) of 1905/13. These were designed by Edwin R Mumford and J Pollock Brown of Denny's experimental ship tank Dumbarton and sponsored by Maurice Denny. The patent was applied for in 1905 and tests were made thereafter. The first 'flight' was made in 1909 with an external power source and the first tethered flight on 6 January 1913, piloted by J Pollock Brown – the first UK piloted flight in a helicopter – just after Cornu and Breguet in France. The Denny company was an inventive shipbuilding and engineering company, designing and constructing commercial hovercraft in the 1960s, maybe a little ahead of their time or the market as they folded soon after.

The first successful flight of the Weir-designed helicopter, (having been preceded by four autogyros, W1-W4) was that of the Weir W5 on 6 June 1938 at Dalrymple, Ayrshire, Weir's home. Its development, the W6, flew on 27 October 1939 at Thornliebank, Glasgow and was the first helicopter to carry a passenger. Both are reputed to have flown over 70 hours each. James Weir was instrumental in developing and promoting rotary-winged flight in this country, in association with the pioneer Juan de la Cierva. Weir became Chairman of the Cierva Autogyro Company, remaining so until around 1966. Cierva himself had been killed in a fixed wing aircraft in 1936.

We should also recognise James Weir's wife, Mora, for she was an equal enthusiast, being the first woman to obtain a flying certificate. She is said to have tested autogyros with Juan de la Cierva and is reputed to be the pilot in one of the photographs of the Weir W3 autogyro. Barbieston Holm in Ayrshire was her flying field.

Just as the understanding of control had been the key to achieving fixed-wing powered flight, so the autogyro provided an insight to helicopter control and paved the way for its successful development, thirty years or so after fixed-wing aircraft. Where would the successful extraction of oil from the North Sea be without the helicopter? – yet at the outbreak of the Second World War the Air Ministry was reported to have told Weirs that it (the helicopter) 'was not likely to be of military use' – again! Hence the cessation of Weir's development work and another opportunity missed.

James G Weir was appointed an Air Commodore in the Royal Air Force Volunteer Reserve. He died in 1973. He must have been one of the very first private flyers in the Glasgow area, since it was seeing him fly from the Moorpark, Renfrew, that caused Captain A C H McLean, 'landings officer' of No 5 Squadron of the newly formed Royal Flying Corps, to select that place as a suitable spot for an airfield. McLean's nephew, Hector, a graduate in law from the University of Glasgow would follow in his footsteps. He was seriously injured in the Battle of Britain, as a pilot in 602 (City of Glasgow) Squadron, Auxiliary Air Force. 602 was lead in that crucial conflict by Squadron Leader (later Air Vice Marshal) Sandy Johnson, a former pupil of Kelvinside Academy.

602's story is an inspiring one and has been told in a number of books and articles. It has a fitting memorial in the 602 Museum Association's museum at Hillington created by the officers and cadets of 2175 (Rolls-Royce) Squadron Air Training Corps, led by their then CO Bill McConnell and opened by the late Marshal of the Royal Air Force, Lord Cameron of Balhousie on 22 October 1983. Alongside it now is the Rolls-Royce Heritage Trust occupying the site of the old engine test-beds where many a 'Merlin' was put through its paces.

Glasgow's Spitfire

James Neil and Ray Baird, two of the team that undertook its restoration

The late war Rolls-Royce 'Griffon' engined Spitfire F21, LA198, which flew with 602 from its reformation in 1947 until its forced landing at Horsham St Faith in July 1949, and which was gifted to the City of Glasgow in 1995, will also make a poignant reminder of the city's illustrious fighter squadron when it is eventually put on display.

Denny/Mumford helicopter 1905 (Patent) 1914
Designed by Edwin R Mumford and flown by J Pollock Brown

James G Weir

His aviator's certificate

*On the left is
Weir's Ceirva autogyro
at Renfrew in 1928
and right
Weir 1 at Abbotsinch
with Juan de la Ceirva at
the controls*

*On the left is the first
Weir helicopter, W5
and right
the second, W6*

Not at all to be forgotten in the same context of 'weekend flyers' is the Scottish Air Division of the Royal Navy Volunteer Reserve – 1830 and later 1843 Squadrons which formed at RNAS Abbotsinch, HMS Sanderling from 1947 under the command of Lieutenant Commander (later Commander) Desmond Murricane who remained CO until the RNVR air squadrons were all disbanded like those of the Royal Auxiliary Air Force in March 1957.

1830 Squadron had distinguished itself early on by winning the FAA's Boyd Trophy in 1949. The Admiralty had wondered whether the weekend flyers would be capable of 'taking to the deck'. Flying from HMS Illustrious in the Firth of Clyde, 1830 completed 196 hours and 205 deck landings without accident and before the advent of the angled deck, a remarkable achievement and testimony to their splendid leadership and superb morale.

The less prominent, but no less committed, 666 Air Observation Post squadron with its three flights 1967 at its HQ at Scone, 1967 at Abbotsinch and 1968 at Turnhouse should also be remembered. Much of their flying was in the field, almost literally so! Two 'weel kent' figures in the city of Glasgow were prominent members: James Fyfe, a former Deacon Convener of the Trades House, and Matthew Neil of the Chamber of Commerce. The AOP squadrons were part of the Royal Auxiliary Air Force though their officers belonged to the Royal Artillery, an echo of the very first days of military flying when it was the airman's lot to spot the fall of shot.

Given Weir's pioneering efforts in rotary-wing flight, it is appropriate for the Department of Aerospace Engineering at the University of Glasgow to have as one of its principal research interests the study of helicopter and autogyro dynamics. It has recently been helping to improve their flying characteristics, working with the Civil Aviation Authority and also with Jim Montgomerie whose company has been building and selling autogyros at Maybole for some years.

The birth of the Royal Air Force was a curious and contentious event, contrary to the established way of doing things in Britain and fought against by both the obvious vested interests and the disinterest of much of the ruling military establishment. Does it, could it, really belong to Glasgow? The answer is YES, in many ways as I shall try to show.

Great Britain's third armed service arose in 1917 amidst a myriad of animosities, personal and professional. Even among its promoters and advocates there was a degree of dissension, distrust and mutual animosity. Against them, unsurprisingly, were the Royal Navy and the Army, both of whom had their own fledgling air arms, the Military and Naval Wings of the overall Royal Flying Corps. And there was a war on, World War One, the greatest conflict in European history. So there was this 'war' within the War where career, personal ambition and envy at least influenced, if not drove, the principal military players. Nothing new there then in the conduct of human affairs.

It took the first aerial attacks on Great Britain during that war to mobilise public opinion and force the government to do something. This it did again in a typically British way by forming a committee – an unusually effective one in this case!

To go back, for a moment, to the previous century – from about 1878 balloons had been used by the Royal Engineers at Woolwich and Chatham and in operations in Bechuanaland during 1884. They had been used for military purposes by the French from the late 18th century, an Aerostatic Corps having been formed on 29 March 1794 within the French artillery. This saw action for observation purposes, at the Battle of Fleurus on 26 June, that year – early evidence of French interest in the air and aviation.,

The Balloon Section, RE, was formed in 1890. Three sections were deployed operationally during the Boer War at the siege of Ladysmith. The evident purpose was to allow commanders to see over the hill and check the fall of shot. David Henderson, as one of the combatants, saw this and was influ-

A balloon of the Aerostatic Corps in action
for observation purposes at the Battle of Fleurus on 26 June 1794

enced by it. It wasn't, however, until 28 February 1911 that an army order led to the establishment of an Air Battalion of the Royal Engineers, on 1 April – No. 1 Company with airships and No. 2 with aeroplanes. The Balloon Factory, having moved from Aldershot in 1905 to Farnborough, became His Majesty's Aircraft Factory in 1911, then the Royal Aircraft Factory in 1912. In 1917 David Henderson considered that 'the industry' was now strong enough to do its own designs and the RAF Factory would concentrate on research. It was subsequently named the Royal Aircraft Establishment, to distinguish it from the new service – a proud and renowned title, foolishly and unnecessarily abandoned as part of the preliminaries to its very questionable privatisation during the 1990s. Its early leaders, successively, Templer, Capper and O'Gorman, are due much more credit than they generally receive. Its erstwhile, early arch-critic, C G Grey of *Aeroplane* magazine, might be pleased though!

During October 1911 aircraft were first used offensively, in a squabble between Turkey and Italy, with questions of moral doubt being expressed as to the use of aerial bombardment.

With some hesitation, but in light of these events, a technical sub-committee of the Committee of Imperial Defence was created in 1912 to deliberate on future policy. Out of this emerged the Royal Flying Corps – established on 13 April 1912, with a Military Wing (Army), a Naval Wing (Navy), a Central Flying School, a Reserve and the Royal Aircraft Factory at Farnborough. Its HQ, chosen by Henderson, was at Upavon in Wiltshire though a number of squadrons were formed at Farnborough. Exactly one month later on 13 May, it assumed the Air Battalion of the Royal Engineers. As might have been expected, the Navy would not readily accept this rather sensible arrangement – indeed, it could be argued, *necessary* arrangement – and plotted from the first to have their own way. Such was its power and influence then that initially, quite without authority, the Royal Naval Air Service, came into being on 1 July 1914 and it should be noted that the very first bombing raids were carried out by the RNAS on German airship bases during 1914.

The position was properly formalised on 29 July 1915 and its 'irregular' title legitimised. Given subsequent events, this might be considered to have been something of a pyrrhic victory or own goal, for the Navy were all too soon to lose effective control of their air service to the fledgling Royal Air Force. The Trenchard/Beatty truce of 1919 and the subsequent Trenchard/Keyes agreement of July 1924 sought to achieve a working arrangement between the senior and junior services with respect to aviation while maintaining the Air Ministry and the Royal Air Force's independence. In the arguments and campaigning of the immediate post-First World War period, Admiral Beatty, a slightly more emollient character than the combative Admiral Keyes, had suggested a compromise line that the Air Force should remain in being with the Navy having its own air capability – which is what ultimately happened though it was not until after the Inskip enquiry of July 1937 that the Navy regained full control of their air forces. In this, Lord Weir was a member of the Balfour Committee and strongly supported the RAF position. Keyes and Trenchard were in fact brothers-in-law! The Admiralty did achieve something from the 1924 agreement when the 'Fleet Air Arm' (of the Royal Air Force) was created with naval officers manning the rear cockpits of naval aircraft, the 'observer' being a particular neccessity for naval operations and regarded as 'the brains'! Inter-service relations were damaged by all of this and, equally, a great deal of practical aviation experience and doctrine was lost to the Navy, and in particular to its future senior officers. The Navy has always held to the idea of being a 'naval officer first and a specialist-submariner or airman second'. Thus it happens that an officer could go from driving a frigate to flying a fast jet on consecutive appointments – remarkable given the widely different handling and knowledge involved.

The Army took no effective part in this inter-service 'war'.

The Admiralty's ultimate victory came perilously close to the outbreak of the Second World War. A heavy price had been paid as naval aviation was something of a poor relation in equipment terms, much more so than even the RAF which had seriously lagged behind during the pacifist 1930s. The industry was consequently equally ill-placed to respond rapidly to naval requirements and eventually the Fleet Air Arm had to be supplied with American aircraft, and excellent many of them were. It might be said that the Admiralty and aviation have not had a particularly productive relationship over the years though there have been many notable personalities and achievements in the face of adversity – how truly British! Admiral of the Fleet Sir Caspar John was the first pilot to reach the highest rank in the Navy, during the 1950s. He was the son of the artist Augustus John, a legendary bohemian and consequently likely to be possessed of a more radical turn of mind.

We returned the compliment post-war when we invented two of the most important developments in carrier aviation – the angled deck and the steam catapult without which high-performance jet aircraft could not easily operate from the deck. The steam catapult was created by Colin Mitchell of Brown Brothers, Edinburgh.

The first German air raids on the UK came as early as December 1914, when an aircraft dropped a small bomb on Dover. This was followed by flights of three Zeppelins on raids against East Coast targets followed by one on London on 31 May 1915, in which there were seven killed and 35 injured. On the night of 2 September, 1916, sixteen Zeppelins attacked London followed by the first raid by German, Gotha bomber aircraft on 28 November. During 1917 there were further attacks, by 23 Gotha GIVs in May and then on 13 June by twenty aircraft dropping 72 bombs, killing 162 with 432 injured. (The last raids were during the night of 19 May, 1918.) In recognition of their traditional role in defending Britain's shores, the RNAS was given the responsibility for air defence. It is hardly to their discredit that they had to find out about it the hard way! The navy had, however, at an operational level, been developing aviation, from as early as 9 May 1912 when Commander Charles Samson had flown a Short S 38 biplane off a wooden platform over the forward gun turret of the cruiser HMS *Hibernia*. The first landing, as has been said, on a ship under way was made by Squadron Commander E H Dunning in a Sopwith Pup on 2 August, 1917, on to the flying-off deck of HMS Furious – sadly he lost his life on the second attempt.

Mention should also be made of the personal, pioneering attempts at flying off the sea in an Avro biplane by Commander Oliver Schwann on 18 November 1910.

In February 1911 the Admiralty, having earlier turned down the Wright Brothers, had begun to take some interest in the air, and accepted Mr Francis McClean's offer to lend them two of his machines for instructional use at his field at Eastchurch. Lieutenants Longmore and Samson became the first official naval aviators.

Naval squadrons fought alongside the RFC in the air war on the Western Front, and also began to do so in the war against the U-boat.

Among the first squadrons of the RFC, at the outset of that terrible conflict, was No 2. It had moved from its base at Farnborough to Montrose in January 1913, initially to Upper

Dysart Farm to the north of the town, then to Broomfield on the south, for anticipated operations in the North Sea area and to be near to operational Naval bases. Montrose was thus the oldest operational airfield in the UK.

Flying off a towed lighter, Lieutenant S D Culley, in a Beardmore, Dalmuir-built Sopwith Camel N6812, downed Zeppellin L53 on 11 August 1918 over the North Sea.

Flight Sub-Lieutenant Warneford had downed the first Zeppelin in the air, over Belgium on 7 June 1915, being awarded the RNAS' first VC. The RFC had its heroes too – Second Lieutenant W B Rhodes-Moorhouse being awarded the first air VC on 26 April 1915 and Leefe Robinson, who downed an attacking Zeppelin near London on the night of 2 September 1916, was also awarded the VC, and subsequently feted by a grateful and thankful public. Major Lanoe Hawker won his VC on 25 July 1915 flying a Barnwell-designed, Bristol Scout 'C'. The 'greats', such as VCs Ball, Mannock and McCudden began to use the basic techniques of air fighting, as pioneered by the German Oswald Boelke and create the legend of the 'fighter pilot', out of their hard-won practical experience. These would last into the Second World War and after.

Naval aviation, nonetheless, did progress and during 1917 Beardmore Dalmuir-built Sopwith Pups, (Type 9901a) flew off and then on to ships at sea – Flight Commander F J Rutland on 28 June from HMS Yarmouth, in the Firth of Forth, and Squadron Commander E H Dunning on to the forward deck of HMS Furious, on 2 August, respectively. The redoubtable Charles Samson had, earlier on, made the first take-off from one of Her Majesty's Ships on 2 May 1912 in a Short S38 biplane.

Interestingly, at the beginning of the War, Frederick Handley Page, then but an embryonic aircraft designer and maker, offered his resources to both the War Office and the Admiralty. He was turned down by the Director, General Military Aviation, our Sir David Henderson, on the grounds of his failure to deliver BE2s on time, and unsurprisingly, taken up by Commodore Murray Sueter, Director of the Air Department of the Admiralty. From this contact arose the development of a strategic bomber, the HP, Type O-100. Contributing to this was the experience of that pioneering naval aviator, Commander Charles Samson, whose early operations on the Continent, in support of the Royal Division, had recognised the need for a 'bloody paralyser (of an aeroplane) to stop the Hun in his tracks'. This was Murray Sueter's commission to Frederick Handley Page and the O-100 became the first in a long series of large bombers produced by that company – so much so that 'Handley Page' became the generic term for a large aircraft! Thus strategic bombing was an RNAS conception. Trenchard's future 'Independent Air Force' of 1918 would rely on the developments of that early type. Handley Page V 1500s were built at Dalmuir and flown from Inchinnan towards the end of the War. The RNAS had engaged in long-range bombing of German industrial targets in 1916: however, the need for their support at the Battle of the Somme caused the cessation of these raids. The last heavy bomber of the Royal Air Force would be the Handley Page Victor, though its final role would be that of aerial refuelling, retiring during the early 1990s after service in the Gulf War.

The main characters in the early development of air power and the independent air service from the extant Royal Flying Corps were David Henderson, the creator of the RFC, Hugh Trenchard, and Frederick Sykes, though the idea of using aircraft for military purposes had occurred to a few other officers including, as has been said, Captain Bertram Dickson.

Higher up there was still little enthusiasm and a clear lack of imagination as to the future role of military aviation. Given Lord Kelvin's previously mentioned jaundiced view of the future of flying in general, this might be understandable if not excusable. This has become par for the course in this country, as witness the experience of Frank Whittle and the jet engine during the 1930s. It has been observed that the jet engine did not emerge from a defence requirement, an airline requirement or an industrial requirement. Nor, for that matter, was it identified in any 'foresight' exercise'. In fact, none of those who would benefit from the existence of the jet engine seemed to recognise its benefits. The future is rarely a linear progression of the past or present. It takes an unusual personal vision, leadership and courage to put aside present concerns and give radical thought as to what might be, and amidst the everyday clamour, hear the 'first trembling footsteps of the future'.

British officialdom during the last century has little to be proud of in its failure to understand and intelligently support indigenous technological development. This is too often exemplified by the attitudes and procedures of H M Treasury. From that allegedly high-powered organisation there has been a consistent lack of well-informed judgement with respect to matters scientific and technological. Is it due to its isolation from the practical realities and consequences of its financial decisions and its sustained ability to overwhelm or outwit their passing political masters? It may also be something to do with the baleful influence of the British, dare I say, English class system, and the peculiarities of our educational priorities which have yet to give science and technology their proper place and consequently have not created a culture of respect and understanding for the engineer or accepted engineering as the great 'art' it is. It is intriguing to know that David Henderson took classes in both arts and science at the University of Glasgow, as was usual in those days.

Engineering had not been readily accepted by universities as a proper subject for study in their hallowed halls. When it was, during the early/middle 19th century, it was organised in collaboration with the relevant professional body and in association with industry and commerce – students and staff spending time working in local firms. Pilcher himself, while an 'assistant' in Naval Architecture from 1891, spent his summers in the drawing office of J&G Thomson, Clydebank – subsequently, the John Brown Shipbuilding and Engineering Company. The University of Glasgow was the first to establish a Chair of Engineering which, after some debate, it did in 1840.

Typically, it has been individuals, often against the odds and the power of the reigning 'establishment', who have saved the day, like Frank Whittle much later on. There does seem to be a kind of collective myopia which affects officialdom in this country which, providentially, does not affect individuals. Small, in organisations and institutions, is not only often beautiful, but more efficient and effective than big!

Contrary to this, perhaps, and surprisingly so, was the rapid formation of the third force, arising from the speedy deliberations of a committee, that usually very British way of avoiding real action. In this case, though, it was a very small committee of effectively only two members, the Prime Minister Lloyd George and General Jan Christian Smuts. Maybe this is why it actually worked! – although the Prime Minister played no active part in the actual process. It was called The Prime Minister's Committee on Air Organisation and Home Defence Against Air Raids. The spur for it was the German air raids from 1914 on the East Coast and on London from 1915, causing growing public outcry and thus political concern. The 'Zepplin menace' was far more difficult to overcome than might now be imagined, given the performance of the early aircraft and the height limitations at which they could operate. Shooting them down was a very skilful and heroic business.

Just why Smuts, an Afrikaaner, though born a British subject in 1870 in South Africa, was chosen by Lloyd George is an intriguing question. He possessed a 'formidable intellect', was a double first honours man from Christ's College, Cambridge and had demonstrable powers of military leadership used previously against the British in South Africa, giving him great credibility for he had been a considerable enemy! He was also independent and trusted. Maybe he had had some useful experience, 'on the other side' of the very early military uses of aviation, balloons, during the Boer War. He was also unusual for someone in high places in, apparently, taking an interest in the use of aviation. He is quoted as saying *'When we reach the mountain summits, we leave behind all the things that weigh heavily on our body and our spirit.*

The 'Zeppelin menace'. Flying off a towed lighter, Lieutenant S D Culley, in a Beardmore, Dalmuir built, Sopwith Camel downed Zeppelin L53 on 11 August 1918 over the North Sea

The statue of Jan Christian Smuts

We leave behind all sense of weakness and depression; we feel a new freedom, a great exhilaration of the body no less than the spirit'. Maybe this gives us a clue as to his outlook relevant to the air. Perhaps it was his evident skill as a negotiator, in helping to draw the second Boer War to a close, when, during negotiations, he was 'taken aside' by Kitchener.

In a remarkable contribution to the 1948, 'Campbell Bannerman' edition of the High School of Glasgow magazine, Smuts pays a fulsome tribute to Campbell Bannerman, newly become Prime Minister – at the time when he himself came to the UK as an emissary in 1905 – crediting Campbell Bannerman with great statesmanship in solving some of the issues in the wake of the Boer Wars and, it may be inferred, being instrumental in converting a sometime enemy into a great ally and subsequent member of the War Cabinet during the First World War. Smuts impressed the British further when, soon after he arrived in London again in March 1917, as South Africa's representative at the Imperial War conference, he was sworn of the Privy Council.

Parliamentary concern with the way things were going in the RFC at the time of the 'Fokker scourge' in the spring of 1916, inflamed by Noel Pemberton Billing MP, gave rise to an enquiry under Mr Justice Bailhache, which heard wild allegations against the Royal Aircraft Factory, Farnborough. Henderson was in the firing line. None of the allegations was found to be true, and the matter proceeded no further. Henderson's articulacy and broad engineering education stood him in great stead at such times and, of course, he fully understood the technical developments in aviation which were proceeding apace. It is the proper job of those democratically elected to enquire into the doings of the administration, civil or military, and the duty of the administration to argue its case and provide the evidence for its policies. At the end of the day, however, Parliament is supreme. By all accounts, Henderson was singularly effective in his advocacy. It was soon to be put to good use.

Neither David Henderson nor William Weir were formally members of the Prime Minister's Committee on Air Organisation and Home Defence Against Air Raids. It did not, as might have been expected, produce a 'fudge' – due perhaps, not only to Jan Christian Smuts' intellect, but also to his independence from 'the establishment', though it might be said that he was rapidly in the process of becoming embraced by it. It was all done without reference to the existing Air Board chaired by Lord Cowdray, who was busily making other plans and who did not support the idea of a separate air service. He soon resigned.

Smuts produced two reports in a matter of weeks: the first concerned itself with the technical aspects of the organisation of air defence; the second provided a case for a new, independent third service, created by an amalgamation of the RFC and RNAS. In these, along with Henderson's July 1917 Memorandum on the Organisations of the Service, lie the genesis of the Royal Air Force. Both were quite short, concise documents comprising of but a few pages. One cannot imagine such a circumstance today!

David Henderson was now replete with much experience of organising and commanding an 'air force' both before and during the war. In his Memorandum, after describing the prevailing administrative arrangements and the inherent dificulties, such as in creating a staff free from parent-service loyalties, he says:

It is difficult to indicate any method of overcoming the present illogical situation of divided responsibility in aeronautics, except by the formation of a complete department and a complete united service dealing with all operations in the air, and with all the accessory services which that expression implies.' Further on, clearly mindful of the general position he states: *'Although logically the desirability of a separate Air Force is almost beyond dispute, yet in its formation many administrative difficulties will have to be overcome, and this will be particularly difficult in time of war.'* And on an optimistic note: *'Personally, I think that if it is decided to form a United Air Service, the more important decisions – if the matter is handled with judge-*

ment – will be accepted without much objection, but that there will be the most violent controversies over the petty details.'[Plus ca change!] Finally: *'To sum up the whole question, it seems only right that I should give a personal opinion. I believe that to ensure the efficiency of the Air Services in the future, they ought to be combined, and that they should be under the control of a Ministry with full administrative and executive powers.*

'The decision, therefore, appears to me to be a speculative one, but only in point of time, for I am convinced that eventually a united, independent Air Service is a necessity.'

(Sgd.) *David Henderson.*
Lieut-General. DGMA
19.7.17

Smuts' report brought about the establishment of an Air Organisation Committee on which Henderson served, relinquishing his post as Director General Military Aeronautics in order to do so. With Smuts, he drafted the Bill for the new Ministry which was placed before Parliament in November 1917 and, without Parliamentary opposition, the Air Force (Constitution) Act of November 1917 allowed for the raising and maintaining of an Air Force Reserve and an Auxiliary Air Force though, understandably, these were not imediate priorities. It was passed and received Royal Assent on 29 November, 1917, a remarkable achievement by any account and despite the inevitable opposition from the vested interests in the Navy and Army, including Trenchard, and his superior, Douglas Haig, Field Marshal, Commander-in-Chief, British Armies in France. The latter, however, was now a believer in the potential and use of air power, unlike so many of his contemporaries. While accepting the inevitable he made his concerns known to the Chief of the Imperial General Staff in a letter on 15 September 1917. In this he was at pains to ensure that air support for the 'armies in the field' would remain 'without danger of causing loss of efficiency'. In a comment on the bombing of civilian populations he says: 'Once such a contest is commenced, however,

Dawn of the Royal Air Force on 1 April 1918. Frank Barnwell's Bristol F 2 B's of 22 squadron
flew the first dawn patrol on that auspicious day on the Western Front

we must be prepared morally and materially to outdo the enemy if we are to hope to attain our ends'.

The recommendations were put into action and the Royal Air Force came into being on 1 April 1918: some high official in the civil service clearly indulged his sense of humour!

What were the arguments advanced by Jan Christian Smuts, illuminated by Henderson's memorandum, which were agreed to and acted swiftly upon by the wartime government – seen against the background of a country being attacked for the first time from the air?

Among his analysis of the current problems affecting the Air Board, the air services and their subordinate position in the military hierarchy he states: *'The time is, however, rapidly approaching when the subordination of the Air Board and the Air Service could no longer be justified. Essentially the position of an air service is quite different from that of the artillery arm; to pursue our comparison, artillery could never be used in war except as a weapon in military or naval or air operations. It is a weapon, an instrument ancilliary to a service, but could not be an independent service itself. Air service on the contrary can be used as an independent means of war operations.'* Finally: *'In conclusion ... Air supremacy may in the long run become as important a factor in the defence of the Empire as sea supremacy.'* His last sentence expresses hope against experience: *'The necessary measures should be defended on the grounds of their inherent and obvious reasonableness and utility, and the desirability of preventing conflict and securing harmony between naval and military requirements.'*

Smuts became a valued ally and ministerial confidant, a role he would continue to play up to and during the Second World War. It would seem that he was just the right man, who happened to be there at just the right time. He died, laden with honours, at his farm in South Africa in 1950. He was described as: 'A scientific humanist by choice, a Christian by conviction'. Churchill said of him, 'He is a magnificent man and one of my most cherished friends'.

In the wake of the Air Force Act, the Air Council and Air Ministry came into being on 2 and 3 January 1918 respectively, and the Royal Air Force itself on 1 April 1918. Lord Rothermere became the first Secretary of State for Air and President of the Air Council, with Henderson as Vice-President. Trenchard became, for a few weeks, the first Chief of the Air Staff: Henderson must have been disappointed not to get the appointment. But dissension reigned. Trenchard, in disagreement with

Rothermere, resigned in March and Henderson soon after. He did not wish to serve with Sykes who had been given the job and who, over the new service's first, crucial year, worked effectively with William Weir, Rothermere's successor. The principal players in the formation of the RAF were now in place with one who would play a crucial role, William Weir, beginning his new career in government. In May 1918 he penned a memorandum setting out 'The Responsibility and Conduct of The Air Ministry.' Thus did Weir begin to lay the administrative foundations for the new service. He did it well!

Lord Rothermere with his brother, Lord Northcliffe, (his predecessor on the Air Board) both powerful newspaper proprietors and proponents of the Empire, had taken a serious interest in the developments in aviation, and in automobiles, from the Wrights' early achievements, using *The Times* and the *Daily Mail* to generate public interest and political action. It has been suggested that around 1915/16 Northcliffe colluded with the War Office and Orville Wright in order to ensure that should the USA enter the War, the American aircraft industry would be aware of current progress and that they should have an effective air force. Curiously, the lead given by the Wrights in the USA had been allowed to slip.

The towering figure of Hugh Montague Trenchard – later the Viscount Trenchard of Wolfeton – is still popularly regarded as 'the father of the Royal Air Force'. He is, however, reported as both disliking that title and indeed disowning it. In a letter to General Sir David Henderson's widow, on the death of Major General Sir Frederick Sykes in 1954, and in response to the latter's obituary in *The Times*, he makes it quite clear that in his opinion, it was Henderson, who was the real 'father'. This, I emphasise, is not in any way to belittle Trenchard's great achievements or the debt which the country and Royal Air Force owes him, but a separate service was not his original conception nor his wish. He had initially seen air power as a means of supporting the army but was to change his views and ensure the Air Force's survival, and create foundations for it after the

Great War when its existence was under sustained attack from, principally, the Royal Navy.

Trenchard served with the Royal Scots Fusiliers and saw much active service abroad – as did Henderson with the Argyll and Sutherland Highlanders. After his South African service and in poorish health, Trenchard's future career in the army did not look too bright but, seeing likely opportunities in the air, he learnt to fly – at the last moment in terms of his age and surprising in view of his fitness. From then on he was committed to the military use of aircraft. At the outset he was, perhaps, more of a tactician than a strategist. His true greatness would come later, after the war, when he would organise and implement air policing, an idea which would ensure the survival of the fledgling Royal Air Force in difficult political circumstances.

Trenchard was a reluctant commander of the Independent (bombing) Air Force set up within the RAF late in the war, on 6 June 1918, and the slogan that 'the bomber would always get through' wielded much, some would say overmuch, influence over future RAF thinking and doctrine up to and during the Second World War. Enthusiasm for strategic bombing however came more from Sir Frederick Sykes than Sir Hugh Trenchard.

After the Armistice, Trenchard offered the Air Minister, Winston Churchill, a more economic plan for the RAF's immediate post-war future than the visionary, expansive Sykes, who had replaced him as Chief of the Air Staff after his and then Henderson's resignations in March 1918, just before the new service's birth. In 1916, Churchill had expressed the view that a full Air Ministry be created rather than the short-lived Air Board under Curzon. During his short time as CAS, Sir Frederick Sykes played a vital role in organising the new service. Trenchard returned to his former post in April 1919 when Sykes, at William Weir's instigation, took over control of civil aviation, then in an embryonic state. Trenchard advocated the idea of imperial policing by the use of aircraft as an effective and economic means of subduing and controlling dissident tribesmen in such parts of the Empire as Mesopotamia and the North-West

Frontier – shades of Kipling and other earlier writers. This was first tried out in British Somaliland during 1919-20. As I write, in 2002, the Royal Air Force continued its 'Operation Southern Watch' over the skies of Southern Iraq, in the wake of 'Operation Desert Storm', 1991, protecting the indigenous Kurdish population from the ruling Iraqi regime. It is an interesting renewal of that original role, though in reverse!

The Iraq War of early 2003 saw the Scottish-based military units given daily billing in the newspapers. 43 Squadron from RAF Leuchars and flying the Tornado F.3 was formed at Stirling in 1916 and flew Frank Barnwell's Bristol Scout 'D' aircraft later that year.

The continual fight to ensure the Air Force's independence may have caused it to be, or seem to be, less helpful in support of the other services than they would have wished, and cause it to be the subject, unjustly perhaps, of some criticism with respect to such events as Dunkirk.

Trenchard's vision for the new service, encompassing proper training arrangements for both air and ground personnel, was given practical realisation in the establishment of the Royal Air Force College at Cranwell and the apprentice training school at Halton. He also introduced the concept of a 'territorial air force' on the lines of a crack cavalry regiment, manned by civilians and based on the main centres of population. The first to be formed was Number 602 (City of Glasgow) Squadron, on 12 September 1925 at Renfrew.

It is curious that Trenchard, who was not a great communicator, managed nevertheless by the force of his presence and personality, combined with the practicality of his vision, to become such a great leader. He was astute politically, a valuable characteristic given the circumstances in the aftermath of the Great War. Perhaps he was not as great a strategist as Sykes or as visionary as Henderson, yet 'Boom' was the right man for the first decade of the fledgling service.

It may be that the terrible experiences of trench warfare on the Western Front may have convinced Trenchard and others,

Fairey IIIF of the Fleet Air Arm over Leuchars in the 1930s

Tornado F3s of 43(F) Squadron from Leuchars, along with G R4s and USAF F-16s on 'Operation Southern Watch', in Southern Iraq – 2002.

Spitfire Ia, 602 (City of Glasgow) Squadron, when based on Westhampnett in June 1940 during the Battle of Britain and flown by Sqn Ldr Sandy Johnstone

Firefly AS6 flown by 1830 1843 Squadrons of the Scottish Air Division of the RNVR when based at Abbotsinch in the early 1950s

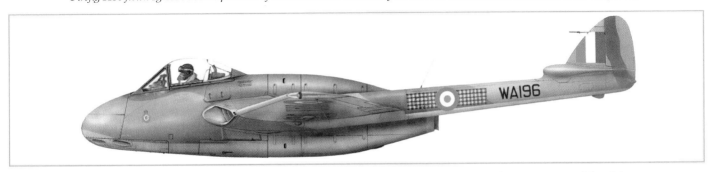

Vampire FB5 jet, flown by 602 Squadron from 1951 until 1957 when the flying squadrons of the RAuxAF were disbanded

such as the future commander of Bomber Command, Arthur Harris, that strategic bombing of economic / industrial targets and its likely demoralisation of the workforce / civilian populace, was likely to be a less costly way for Great Britain to wage a future war, and that even the threat of bombing might prevent one.

If not the 'father' of the RAF, Trenchard, was assuredly the person who ensured the fledgling service's survival and gave it the soundest of foundations and upbringing. These foundations would endure: they were well-laid and have served effectively in times of war and in times of peace. They were the true legacy and glory of a big man who, in the beginning, had been somewhat sceptical of the air service he would go on to serve with such distinction and dedication. It was he also, who, in October 1919 founded the Royal Air Force Benevolent Fund. There is real substance in the legend that has been created around him, flavoured with some mythology. He died in 1956. The development of air power owes much to him.

The personal relationship – rivalry in career terms – between Henderson and Sykes deteriorated as the war progressed as did that between Trenchard and Sykes, no doubt related to the former.

Professional competitiveness and genuine differences of view fuelled the personal animosities. Sykes was clearly a cleverer man than Trenchard, and was a true strategic thinker. He would seem to have lacked, however, the kind of robust leadership and physical presence, charisma perhaps, which the inarticulate Trenchard possessed. Neither did he enjoy the superb services of an urbane Maurice Baring as secretary and personal assistant. Sykes's own significant contribution to the development of air power seemed to have been rather unjustifiably, deliberately downplayed, even disparaged, in the years after the First World War. The 'Trenchard legend' has been powerful, persistent and persuasive in the collective hearts and minds of the Royal Air Force throughout its existence, for the most part justifiably with respect to his time as CAS after his

false start. He was not, however, its 'father.'

It is intriguing to wonder why, given fellow Glaswegian Weir's influence, Henderson, who as Vice-President of the new Air Board had worked closely with Weir on the early proposals for the new service, had not been appointed its first Chief of Staff rather than Trenchard. Lord Rothermere was, at the time still in the Chair. It has been said that Weir had been 'plagued' by Henderson, and Weir's view was maybe influenced by the squabbling he witnessed as Controller of Aeronautical Supplies, between the War Office and the Admiralty over aircraft design and production. Perhaps Weir recognised in Sykes the great organising ability and skill in management that Weir himself possessed and which he would have realised was then needed. Equally, he saw in Trenchard the kind of personal leadership subsequently required to maintain the new, 'peacetime' service. Henderson had resigned shortly after Trenchard over the latter's lack of confidence in Rothermere as Air Minister. Rothermere himself resigned shortly after to be replaced by Weir. Henderson said that he would be unable to work with Sykes when Sykes was appointed CAS after Trenchard's March 1918 resignation. Henderson's role in the third service was crucial through his advice to Smuts, yet he was to become increasingly sidelined, maybe on health grounds, so far as air matters were concerned. His juniors, Sykes and Trenchard, took major commands. Weir himself saw off the attacks on the independence of the Air Force from the Navy, in 1923, before leaving the political, military arena, at least for the time being. What did happen to aviation in the navy, however, was unfortunate in that its proper aviation requirements went largely by the board and it was to be very ill-equipped to face future conflict.

As we know, throughout its existence, and maybe even today, the Royal Air Force's independence has occasionally been challenged, so far as maritime operations are concerned and by the Army in their support. The beginning of the 21st century, in fact, sees significant collaborative ventures being planned and instigated, 'joint' being the current buzzword, with respect to inter-service training and the operational control of certain air assets, for example, combining the RN and RAF Harrier forces and the services' helicopter training arrangements in which all three services participate, with, however, civilian contractors doing the job. The ruling, powerful driving force in all of this is, unsurprisingly and as always, cost. Whether true value will really be obtained will not be seen until the systems have been fully tested in operations. Lessons learnt from recent wars and from the continuing and increasing peace-keeping deployments have yet to be acknowledged in the public domain. After 11 September 2001 anti-terrorist operations are set to become a principal task for our military. In times of relative peace, the British public are somewhat ambivalent in their attitude to their armed forces. It took bombs to fall on London in 1915 for the message of air power to impinge upon public awareness for the first time.

The Royal Air Force's proud motto was hardly the result of great deliberation. When its predecessor, the RFC's, first commander of the military wing, Captain (temporary Major) Frederick Sykes from the 15th Hussars asked for suggestions. one of his officers, J S Yule came up with the motto of the Irish Mulvaney family in H Rider Haggard's, *The People of the Mist*. 'Through Struggle to the Stars' – 'Per Ardua ad Astra' was adopted. It has served well!

Against the awful scenario of the First World War, at the very beginning of the development of powered flight, and amidst inter-service rivalries, the inauguration of the new service happened surprisingly quickly. No great occasion marked its birth nor trumpets heralded its coming. The Bristol Fighters of 22 Squadron, designed by Frank Barnwell from Balfron and Stirling, flew the first dawn patrols on that auspicious day in 1918 from Vert Galand airfield, on the Western Front. Thus, without ceremony, was the new service committed to the fray. 'Per Ardua ad Astra' indeed! In reality, little if anything had changed, even with the absorption of the RNAS.

The press of the day seemed to ignore the occasion of the Royal Air Force's birth. 1 April 1918 was Easter Monday and *The Times* made no mention of the new arrival but gave lengthy coverage to the King's visit to his army in France. He had bumped into a group of 'Highlanders' from the 51st Division sitting by the roadside and had been cheered by them. He had also called on the HQ of the 'Royal Flying Corps' and 'at several aerodromes'. At one of these were men of Captain James McCudden's squadron, though he himself was not present. They were pleased to be told of McCudden's award of the Victoria Cross. McCudden would subsequently serve at the School of Air Fighting, Turnberry. *The Times* still carried the tittle-tattle of the toffs.

The *Glasgow Bulletin* for that Monday headlined, 'In the great battle there is now co-ordination as well as co-operation', along with 'Fierce German attack'. It was the Spring weekend in Glasgow!

The *Daily Record* and *Daily Mail*, a few days later, reported 'useful work for women' with a photograph of some girls beside an aeroplane: 'The Women's Legion is doing good work organising training'. Typical of the period, its front page carried advertising and on that day Treron's, of Sauchiehall Street, were prominently pushing their April displays of 'Millinery Gowns Costumes Coats Lingerie Corsets'!

Even the *Glasgow Herald* sounded no trumpet for the fledgling service, seemingly unaware of its fellow citizens' part in its conception and creation.

Glaswegians have traditionally made 'bonny fechters'. Their contribution to the armed forces has been second to none and although in times of peace the public's attitude generally to the military is somewhat mixed, there still remains a pride in the recorded story of the courage, heroism and commitment of its people, civil and military, in the dismal times of war. The Iraq War of 2003 saw a considerable presence of Scottish-based military units.

The Highland Light Infantry (City of Glasgow Regiment)

David Henderson 'Father' of the Royal Air Force

has a proud history and Glaswegians have served, and still serve, in many of the Army's remaining famous regiments. The men and women of Clydeside also produced many of the Royal Navy's finest warships and, remarkably, still do though in much reduced circumstances.

Few however realise that the third service, the Royal Air Force, owes much of its existence to those two Glaswegians, David Henderson and William Weir – Henderson for his understanding and articulate advocacy of air power and its potential, as seen from the professional military standpoint, and Weir, sharing that outlook from a political, industrial and organisational position.

David Henderson was born in Glasgow in 1862 into a West of Scotland shipping/engineering family. He enrolled into the University of Glasgow in 1877 at the age of 15 (being taught reputedly by Kelvin), taking classes during his first year in Arts which, in those days, encompassed maths, physics, civil engineering and mechanics, office and field work in engineering and English literature. What a pity he was too early to meet Walter

Raleigh who would, in the future, be recounting his deeds in the Flying Corps. He spent the next two sessions studying astronomy, chemistry and geology. Apparently he did not graduate. Not unusual then, and maybe there are lessons for us in this today, in terms of the value of a broad education, but what would our present masters have to say about non-completion!

Leaving the University in 1881, he joined the Army, being gazetted into the Argyll and Sutherland Highlanders and posted to Capetown in 1883. He was to see much action during the Zulu wars and was regarded as a popular officer. Photographs of him show him cutting a rather elegant figure. He married Henrietta Caroline, second daughter of Henry Dundas, and grandaughter of the first Lord Napier of Magdala (of Indian Mutiny fame who, on ignoring his orders, captured Sind and signalled memorably: 'Peccavi' – 'I have sinned'!).

Henderson saw further action in the Sudan with Kitchener, and in the Boer Wars. During the latter, he witnessed the use of balloons for reconnaissance and, though realising their limitations, saw the military potential of 'aircraft'. Thus began what would become his great contribution to the future of warfare.

In 1904, soon after the Wrights' 1903 triumph at Kitty Hawk, he produced his first book, *Field Intelligence, its Principles and Practice*, followed in 1907 by *The Art of Reconnaissance* – truly significant at the time though perhaps not yet recognising the offensive possibilities of aeroplanes as Dickson subsequently did. In fact, his view was that though the aircraft could be useful for 'scouting', it had no practical role to play within the Empire.

David Henderson learnt to fly in 1911 at the Bristol School of Flying, Brooklands, doing so under the name of 'Henry Davidson', and received his Royal Aero Club Certificate, No 118 on 17 August. The formation of the RFC on 13 April 1912 gave the means for Henderson to advance his interest in the air. It also provided the necessary opportunities to Captain Frederick H Sykes. He would become a colleague and, perhaps, in Henderson's eyes, a rival. The two were destined to march together but not always in step, particularly later on. Henderson was a man of great personal charm. Sykes would not seem to have shared this attribute, yet was undoubtedly a great organiser, maybe what we would call a great manager. He was to fall foul of Trenchard, perhaps partly as a result of the animosity between Sykes and Henderson. He must have made his mark with Weir, however, as after Trenchard's resignation on 19 March 1918, just before the birthday of the Royal Air Force, he was appointed Chief of the Air Staff.

Henderson became Director of Military Training on 1 July 1912 and Director General of Military Aviation on 1 September 1913. In August of 1912 aeroplane trials had been conducted on Salisbury Plain, with Henderson and Sykes participating. During the Army manoeuvres of that year with Sykes, now commandant of the RFC, Haig, leading the attacking force instructed one of his majors to: 'Tell Sykes he is wasting his time'. Even in 1914 he maintained the view that mounted cavalry would not be supplanted by the aeroplane – 'the horse would have as much use in the future as it ever had in the past'. Experience would soon alter that view.

On 4 August 1914, Brigadier General David Henderson took the RFC to France, to fight. His Chief of Staff was Frederick Sykes. The wisdom of combining command of the Corps in the field with the position of DGMA at home can be questioned. Henderson's health wasn't good, making the situation worse and leading to his replacement by Brigadier Hugh Trenchard on 7 August 1915. Henderson returned to the UK continuing as DGMA.

Having served on the Air Organisation Committee, Henderson became Vice-President of the Air Council in 1918, but subsequently resigned in 1918 along with Trenchard, after the disagreements with Rothermere thus severing his service with the Air Force. He went back to France in August 1918 as Area Commandant, British Army, then as Military Counsellor in the British Embassy in Paris. In June 1919, having left the Army, he became Director General of the League of Red Cross in Geneva. Ill health continued to trouble him and he died on 17 of August 1921, ten years to the day after he qualified as a pilot.

He was buried in Girvan, alongside his only son Ian – not far from Turnberry aerodrome where Ian, aged 21, had been killed in a flying accident, at No 1 Fighting School on 21 June, 1918. He was taking off in a DH9, D1080, with Lieutenant Herbert Redler, a South African from Capetown. Many other families involved in aviation had and would suffer similar tragedies. Captain Ian Henderson MC had served with his father's old regiment before joining the RFC. He had a distinguished record, being credited with seven victories, and was awarded the Military Cross.

David Henderson is represented in the Royal Air Force Museum at Hendon through a fine bronze bust by Malvina Tollman. An obituary written by C G Grey, a sometime critic of Henderson's and of many of his contemporaries' policies, stated: *'It was he who first among General Officers realised the vital importance of Military Aviation and took the first steps to set up a separate corps to develop the new arm. British air power will always owe its first debt of gratitude to David Henderson.'*

Henry Probert, former Head of the Air Historical Branch of the MoD, writes in his book *High Commanders of the Royal Air Force*:

'It was Henderson who, having qualified to fly at the age of 49, commanded the Royal Flying Corps in France in 1914 and later represented it on the Army Council. By 1917 he had no doubt that there must be a united air service under an independent Air Ministry, a view which he stated unequivocally to General Smuts. He then worked on the Air Organisation Committee and in 1918 became Vice-President of the Air Council, from which he resigned, just after Trenchard.'

After Sir Frederick Sykes' death in 1954 his obituary in *The Times* credited him with being 'the father of the RFC'. Lord Trenchard wrote to Lady Henderson correcting that view. *'Sir David was the man whose influence at the War Office and whose great strength of character made him the power in air matters that he was.'* – a view supported by (Marshal of the Royal Air Force) Sir

Edward Ellington in a letter to *The Times* of 4 October 1954, in which he writes that Henderson *'was well placed to use with great effect his great powers of imagination, clear exposition and tact to persuade the Army Council that they could no longer afford to neglect this new weapon or starve its development. It is entirely owing to Henderson's persistence that the RFC Committee was formed.'*

David Henderson is a man in whom the City of Glasgow and its ancient University can take justifiable pride. In his *Times* obituary it was also said that: *'Sir David Henderson performed services for which this country should always be grateful.'* Harald Penrose wrote of him that [he] *'was instrumental in forming the RFC where his sympathetic and well disciplined mind made him ideal in shaping the new service.'* His subsequent contribution to the establishment of the Royal Air Force was even greater. We should accord him his due.

It might be wondered whether the UK now has the industrial capability required to conduct any kind of sustained conflict even, as is anticipated, in concert with allies. Recent engagements suggest that levels of available weaponry are very low and their replenishment uncertain. Our own capacity is being steadily reduced as witness the closure of the ordnance factory at Bishopton with the proposal to purchase future supplies of its products from foreign sources. Will war, on any strategic level, become increasingly impossible to sustain because of a lack of industrial capacity, or the economic wherewithal to provide the material? Even the 'military/industrial complex' with its sinister connotation, in the USA, may be difficult to maintain. It was economic considerations which brought about the collapse of the former Soviet Union in the late 1980s as it was simply unable to sustain the military might to compete with the West, while trying to satisfy the basic needs of its people. What is clear is that, more than ever, military procurement is as much to do with political and economic matters as with the satisfaction of actual service needs. Some recent decisions regarding new

aircraft for the RAF have been seen as being based politically rather than on what would be the best for that service's requirements. Of course, in the last thirty years or so, major projects have, on cost grounds, involved international partnerships and collaborative agreements: Concorde, Jaguar and Tornado, in their different ways, have been successful, yet the French, while collaborating in their own inimitable way in some projects, have managed to produce their own hardware such as the successful Dassault range of fighter aircraft with today's Rafale, a competitor to our Eurofighter.

William Weir's own firm became a major source of aircraft production during the First World War as did a number of Clyde shipyards including Barclay Curle, together with other engineering firms. Outstandingly, Beardmore's not only built many aircraft for the RNAS and RAF under licence, but established its own design section and subsequently a Reserve flying school at Renfrew. The latter had been developed as an airfield to become an Acceptance Park for aircraft built around Glasgow for, principally, the RFC. Beardmore's had its own park at Inchinnan but also test flew their aircraft from a field, Robertson's Park, adjacent to their factories at Dalmuir. It was there that the airship R34 and others were built, to be first flown over the river at Inchinnan.

In 1928 Beardmore's produced at Dalmuir the giant 'Inflexible' monoplane, Britain's largest landplane until the Bristol 'Brabazon' of the late 1940s, and an 'Inverness' flying boat both using the German Rohrbach all-metal method of construction. One of the latter had already been produced by Rohrbach themselves in 1925, yet this country's aircraft industry was content to continue designing and making wood and fabric biplanes well into the 1930s long after Beardmore's earlier experiments and indeed Junkers production civil aircraft from 1924.

In the USA Boeing, Lockheed and notably Douglas had begun the production of modern all-metal monoplanes for their airlines from 1932.

It was in Germany that the first passenger aircraft was flown

Beardmore's largest plane the Inflexible, 1928

Beardmore's smallest plane the Wee Bee, 1924

on 19 June 1910, the twenty-seater airship Delag Zeppelin LZ 7 *Deutschland*.

The world's first scheduled passenger flight was made on 1 January 1914, carrying one passenger initially then two, from St Petersburg to Tampa in Florida, USA.

From *Ode to the Beardmore Inflexible*

Oh, beautiful new metal monoplane built on the silvery Clyde,
With your three 650-horsepower Rolls-Royce Condor engines,
whose power cannot be denied,
And your great duralumin wings of 15 feet 7 inches span,
You are destined for success, deny it who can.
Though you were designed by Messrs Rohrbach in the land of Germany,
It has taken the skill of the Beardmore firm to make you a reality.
Designer William Shackleton has brought you to perfection,
And his great accomplishment is widely acclaimed from every direction.

At the RAF Display at Hendon on June the 30th, so I've heard,
You cast a massive shadow, like some prehistoric bird;
Wherever you go, people will acclaim your name,
Saying: 'There goes the great Inflexible, that aeroplane of fame',
And though you are a little on the heavy side, I fear,
You will leave a great impression that will last for many a year,
And all who see you you will not deride,
But sing your praises, metal eagle of the Clyde.

by Philip (McGonagall) Jarrett 1988

Sadly, Beardmore's was too far away from the centre of power in London so what could have been the start of a Scottish aircraft industry was finally closed down in 1929, at the beginning of the world economic depression and after a second attempt to make a go of it. There was also some concern in official circles over political activism on Clydeside, influenced by the legend of the 'Red Clyde'. Among those who had served Beardmore's was one James Hamilton. He had studied at the 'Tech' and on Beardmore's closure he joined Handley Page rising to become its production director and responsible for its massive wartime effort.

William Beardmore, later the first Lord Invernairn, was a remarkable individual for the range of engineering products which his company made – ships, locomotives, internal combustion engines, aircraft and airships along with his great forge at Parkhead.

Beardmore's factory at Dalmuir on the banks of the Clyde

Aviation Department at Beardmore's, Dalmuir, 1927

Lord Trenchard's visit to Beardmore's, Dalmuir
he is wearing the light overcoat. Lord Weir stands last on the right

Muirhead Bone's drawing of aircraft assembly at Beardmore's

Beardmore's flying field, Robertson Park with Camel 2F1's

Beardmore's fighter for the Latvian Airforce, 1925

The 'Tondern Raid', August 1918 by Beardmore built Sopwith 2F1 Camels flying from HMS Furious
The first such raid from a ship at sea

If David Henderson did so much to create the new air service, then Frank Barnwell did much to provide it with the aeroplanes it needed from before the First World War until just before the Second. His brother Harold also made a distinguished contribution as a pioneer pilot and designer. Archibald, the youngest brother, inclined more to administrative work and became a local councillor in Bridge of Allan. He had been commissioned in the Army, serving in the Great War, and achieving the rank of Major.

Their father, Richard Barnwell senior, was born at Canterbury in 1849. He married, in 1877, the step-sister of the wife of Sir William Pearce, senior partner in the Randolph Elder shipbuilding and engineering company of Govan. They had three sons and four daughters. Richard Harold was born in 1878, Frank Soutar in 1880 and Archibald in 1882. Regrettably, little seems to be recorded about the daughters. The family home was in Lewisham before their move to Glasgow in 1881 when Richard Barnwell became a junior partner in Elder & Company. He had trained with the Union Bank in London. It would seem that Pearce had chosen him as his successor as in 1886 he was appointed managing director of what was now the Fairfield Shipbuilding and Engineering Co. Ltd. That he was married to the step-sister of Lady Pearce no doubt helped! What would we and today's press make of that, I wonder. And what would these pioneer aviators now make of the Fairfield ship-building yard which, after a long and at times difficult existence, has become a part of the UK's largest aerospace organisation, BAE SYSTEMS!

Richard Barnwell assumed a number of other major business involvements, including being chairman of the Herne Bay Pier Company, directorships of a number of steamship companies, and membership of the local board of the Royal Insurance Company – a considerable personage by all accounts.

Sadly, Richard Barnwell died at Elcho House on 7 March 1898 after a long illness, through which he was tended by his sister, Miss Elizabeth Ann Barnwell. His funeral took place on

Frank Barnwell

the 11th, and he was laid to rest in Craigton Cemetery, Glasgow. He was described as having 'a thoroughly gentlemanly and catholicity of character – esteemed and respected by all classes'. Elcho House, Balfron, remained the Barnwells' home until Frank, in 1909, rented 'Oakville', in Bridge of Allan. Elcho House became, as it is now, 'Auchendarroch House' around 1910.

Around Richard Barnwell's time, Percy Pilcher was undertaking his apprenticeship at the shipyard between 1 June 1887 and 8 July 1889, which he then followed with five months at Cairns & Co., Glasgow, as an apprentice moulder. He became well known for his ideas, inventiveness and interest in flight. Might this, in particular his ambition to conceive a flying machine, have been conveyed by Barnwell senior to his sons over the dinner table at the family home? Was this how the seeds were sown in the imaginations of Harold and Frank?

Of the three sons of of Richard Barnwell, Harold, Frank and Archibald, it fell to the first two to be bitten by the aviation bug. They were educated at Fettes College and, though it has been said that their academic record was less than outstanding, in 1896 Harold achieved third place in maths and second in Latin, with his younger brother Frank coming first in maths and, in my view significantly, second in drawing. Archie also demonstrated some prowess in drawing.

Drawing is the universal language of design in all its variants whether using a simple lead pencil, one of the greatest of all inventions, or manipulating the very latest in electronic image making. It is the means by which designers first communicate with themselves through giving concrete form to that will o' the wisp idea in the mind's eye. It is the way that a design is first firmed-up and then evaluated. It is the means whereby the nature, specification, details and requirements of the chosen design is transmitted to those who will make it. It can even be a thing of beauty in its own right.

We now value many of the Victorian engineers' drawings for their aesthetic qualities even though the original reasons for their attractive presentation was functional – to best explain what it was that was portrayed and intended to be made. Thus what was once done for purely practical purposes has now become an object of artistic appreciation and satisfaction in itself.

It is quite evident from examining some of the childhood drawings of our greatest engineers such as Brunel, Gresley and many others that their ability to draw and to sketch accurately, and to convincingly portray what they had in mind, lay at the heart of their subsequent success as designers. Look, too, at Pilcher's fine drawings, some done when he was a Naval officer – a requirement before the days of easy photography in order to record topographical and other features for potential military

Pilcher's drawing of 'Calypso' getting main yard fore and aft, 30 August 1862

purposes and a vital reconnaissance tool. Frank Barnwell's skill as a draughtsman was thus a clear, early sign of his fertile, practical imagination and possible future career.

There is a present danger with the easily available, superficial sophistication of the computer that *it* is allowed to design. The results of this are all too evident in print where the familiar trade marks of particular computer software are depressingly common. It is the mark of professional laziness. Machines make good slaves but poor masters.

Harold worked in the new Argyll Motor works at Alexandria in the Vale of Leven, not far from where Pilcher flew, while taking evening classes at the Glasgow and West of Scotland Technical College. (Although now the University of Strathclyde it was still known affectionately, and with respect, to many all over the world as the 'Tech'.) He attended there during 1897/98 and 1898/99.

Frank, similarly, attended the Tech evening classes during 1898/99 and 1899/1900. His occupation was given as 'draughtsman', and his address as 3 Buckingham Square, Govan. He went

The Barnwell aircraft No. 1 of 1905 at Elcho House, Balfron

The 1909 'Big bi-plane', at Causewayhead

on to complete a degree in Naval Architecture at the University of Glasgow, graduating in 1905. Percy P would have approved!

There was, until quite recent times, a strong and distinguished practice of technical education by evening class combined with practical instruction and experience during the day on the shop floor. Apprenticeships are still available but are much diminished in number as both industry declines and governments seek to greatly increase the complement of those in full-time higher and further education to 50% of the eligible population.

Maybe it was seeing Henri Farman undertaking gliding experiments in south-east France during a holiday there that provided the true genesis of the Barnwell brothers' enthusiasm to fly. At any rate, Harold and Frank began experimenting with model gliders at Elcho House around 1905 and did build a full-size biplane there at that time. It was powered by a Peugeot motor-cycle engine and did not fly. Both Harold and Frank had been apprentices in their father's shipyard, however Harold moved to the nascent Argyll Motor Works in Alexandria, a substantial though ill-fated concern. Its splendid building still stands as a kind of monument to another of Scotland's might-have-been, should-have-been, great industries.

Frank went off to the USA to see what might be learnt there

and to broaden his experience by working in a Boston shipyard. While in the USA he met the Wright brothers and was no doubt impressed by their aeronautical achievements. It is perhaps difficult for us now to comprehend how little was generally known about them over here and in Europe. Charles H Gibbs-Smith refers to the 'rebirth of European Aviation' around 1908, particularly in France where so many attempts at aviating had been made during the 19th century – though the retrospective claims of Clement Ader for powered flight after his October 1890 'hop' in his 'Eole', and the 1897 attempts in his 'Avion 111', are not sustainable. French interest in the Wrights' achievements did not reawaken until around 1906 with the Brazilian-born Santos-Dumont's flight in his 14 bis. Yet some of the French were unwilling to accord the Wrights proper recognition as the first men to truly fly, heavier-than-air machines. This, despite that 'grand old man' of American aviation, the French-born Octave Chanute's lecture to the Aero-Club of France on 2 April 1903 when he dealt with current progress and when, as a strong supporter of the Wrights and knowing their activities (in gliding), he informed his audience of their 'message'.

French opinion was to take the superior line that they had progressed quite independently, owing nothing to the Wrights, but the visit of Wilbur Wright to France, from May 1908, did much to convince most French aviators. 'For us in France and everywhere, a new era in mechanical flight has commenced it is marvellous,' exclaimed Louis Bleriot. 'Who can now doubt that the Wrights have done all they claimed?' asked Rene Gasnier. Others, particularly the Voisins, remained unreasonably hostile. The French, like many on the British side of the Channel, did not seem to grasp the essential question of three-axis control, the key to powered flight and central to the Wrights' success. The Wrights achieved lateral control by twisting the wing tips – wing warping. This was soon replaced by ailerons – hinged surfaces on the outer trailing edges of the wings. Intriguingly, one hundred years on, the original idea is making a reappearance in the sophisticated form of 'surface morphing' – altering the wing camber as a means of control.

By 1909 the Wrights were duly accorded the honour and glory that was properly theirs and aviation in Europe began again, for real. Louis Bleriot's epic crossing of the English Channel on 25 July is regarded by Gibbs-Smith as being a direct result of the Wright demonstrations. 'That Wilbur Wright is in possession of a power which controls the fate of nations, is beyond dispute,' was the view of Major B F S Baden-Powell, then Secretary of the Aeronautical Society of Great Britain – now the Royal Aeronautical Society. Orville and Wilbur Wright had been awarded the Society's first two Gold Medals in 1908.

For the Barnwells in 1907, with Frank's return from the States, it was a new start, with an engineering business at Causewayhead, Stirling – the Grampian Engineering and Motor Company. It was still there, nearly a century later though involved in structural engineering. It would seem that, of the brothers, Harold was a director with both Frank and Archie described as 'secretary'. The company seems to have arisen out of John Simpson Engineers, of Whins of Milton, Bannockburn. This company was closed in April 1907 and the Grampian Engineering and Motor Company established in May. John Simpson became a director of the latter. Their products included a flash steam boiler suitable for motor cars and laundry equip-

ment. No doubt using Harold's experience at the Argyll company, they also engaged in designing and making engines to be incorporated in third parties' coachwork, and other aspects of motor engineering. A W McHardy who had been employed by Fairfields and a Brigadier Oliver, formerly of the Royal Engineers at their depot in Stirling, were also on the new company's Board.

It was on that foundation that Harold and Frank Barnwell renewed their fascination for flying. In a hangar at Cornton farm, the brothers constructed a monoplane during 1908. Attempts to fly it in December proved unsuccessful. Undeterred, during 1909 they went on to build what they described as a 'Wright-type' biplane, their 'big biplane'. Big and ungainly it certainly seemed to be, without the elegant simplicity of the Wright aircraft, but fly it did, for 80 yards at a height of 12 feet, on 29 July 1909 – just two weeks after Bleriot's channel crossing and A V Roe's first 'official', all-British flight down south. It proved however to be 'cumbersome and expensive to repair'. Given that the Wrights had produced by 1905 a truly reliable flying machine and demonstrated its capabilities beyond any doubt, it is surprising that European builders were still struggling to emulate them in 1909. Two other aircraft were built during 1910, but little of them seems to be known or recorded.

It was their sixth machine, built that year, that was to be the star. A return to the monoplane configuration produced a remarkably advanced aeroplane, in comparison with the previous biplane. It was first flown on 14 January 1911 by Harold, who managed 600 yards and a height of 50 feet before landing upside down in a ploughed field – par for the course then for those who would fly! On the 30th, with Harold again flying, and in the presence of the officials of the Scottish Aeronautical Society, the monoplane flew for 1 minute and 2.4 seconds, covering a distance of over one mile and consequently winning the Society's J R K Law Prize. This had been offered for the first all-Scottish aeroplane to make a flight of more than half a mile.

We should, however, set that achievement against what had

Harold Barnwell was Vickers' chief test pilot

The Barnwell monoplane No, 6 outside the Casewayhead hanager.
Ready for takeoff from the airfield in Causewayhead in 1911 and flying.
The design looked remarkably advanced

been done elsewhere, ie Bleriot's Channel flight nearly a year and a half previously and the various successful aircraft which were demonstrated at the first Scottish flying meet at Lanark from 6 to 13 August 1910. Bleriot-type aircraft being much in evidence. Similar types were also being offered around that time by Scottish makers including W S Pollock of Glasgow and the 'Caledonia' monoplane, from the Scottish Aviation Company of Barrhead. It should also be noted that in January 1908 Henri Farman won the 50,000 franc Grand prix d'Aviation at Issy near Paris for flying more than a kilometre, in a circle.

What is particularly striking about the Barnwell 1910/11 monoplane aircraft is just how advanced a design it looked. It is not clear however, what, if any, were the arrangements for lateral control – how well did the Barnwells understand the crucial control issue? The previous 'big biplane' had what might seem to be a kind of aileron arrangement (though ailerons were yet to appear), but the new monoplane did not. It has been suggested

that wing-warping was employed on the monoplane. It seems likely, as the Barnwells must have been well enough aware of the basic control. *Flight* magazine gave an illustrated page over to the Barnwells in its issue of 18 February 1911, sniffily saying that: 'Mr Barnwell and the Grampian Motor Works, with which he is associated, have been experimenting in aeroplane work and the success that has attended his efforts at last is the result of a great deal of personal experience necessarily obtained very largely by trial and error, inasmuch as the work is being carried on in a place that is not exactly qualified to rank as yet as a centre of aviation in England'. We can see from this why Scottish pioneers had difficulty in achieving their due recognition – they were too far from London, an auld problem which still has its echoes today. Maybe Holyrood will sort it!

The Wrights' particular method of achieving lateral control by wing-warping would prove to be short-lived, as ailerons would soon be shown to be the real way forward: however in realising that body/weight-shift, as used by Lilienthal and Pilcher, could not provide sufficient authority for the heavier, powered machine they demonstrated their fundamental grasp of the main issue involved.

It's an intriguing thought that Pilcher, though working in an academic environment, seemed to approach the business in a rather whimsical, seat-of-the-pants sort of way. He did, however, suggest in this account from his experience of weight-shift that he was reflecting upon the control issue: 'Once when sailing fast I saw I was going to land in a big bush, so getting back a little in the machine I was able to rise a little and pass quite clear of the bush (although it was quite calm at the time); and I have also been able to steer sideways to a limited extent by moving the weight of my body towards the side to which I wanted to turn'. He goes on to say: 'This is the first machine in which I have had any wheels, which are a great convenience for moving the machine about, and often save the framework from getting broken if one lands clumsily.'

The Wrights, on the other hand, scions of the New World, had not felt the need to formally graduate from high school, but were scientific and methodical in their approach, from the 1899 kite to the 1900 kite/glider, and to the 1901 glider. Perhaps it was the influence of their mother, a mathematician, for on checking Lilienthal's calculations they found them to be incorrect and, after experiencing problems with the 1901 glider, they built a wind tunnel to provide them with a valuable research tool. The 1902 glider, containing the fruits of their careful experiments, was the world's first fully controllable aircraft and led the way to the triumph of the powered 'Flyer' of 1903 and then, not without difficulty, to the world's first truly practical aircraft of 1905, the 'Dayton Flyer' and the public flights in 1908. They had, up to then, avoided unnecessary public exposure to protect their inventions.

It is little wonder that they succeeded in conquering the air in such a short time, from 1899 to 1903. That date, though marking the first true powered flight, was a staging point in the

The Wright Brothers, Orville, left and Wilbur at an air meet in 1909

Wrights' development between 1899 and 1905. Their machine of the latter date was in reality the first practical aircraft.

Photographs of the two brothers show them to be rather serious, very proper gentlemen in their bowler hats and stiff collars. Bicycle makers were in a particularly good position, of course, to design and build the necessary lightweight structure

as the bicycle is the most efficient means of converting human energy into work, and thus the best likely structure given the low power available for these early aircraft.

From May to September 1911 the Barnwell monoplane was exhibited at the great Glasgow Exhibition after which some flights were accomplished at Blairdrummond – a flight of five miles at 200 feet on 13 October and twice at Cambusdrenny on the 17th.

Harold Barnwell went down to the Vickers Flying School at Brooklands to receive his Royal Aero Club Certificate, No 278 on 3 September, 1912. His prowess was such that he became an instructor there and, later, Chief Instructor, serving between 1912 and 1914. In 1913 he gave freelance flying lessons to Noel Pemberton Billing who was to cause much trouble to David Henderson a few years later.

Between 1912 and August 1914 the school trained 77 pilots, a record for such an establishment – 36, between January and August 1914 alone. Among them was one Hugh Dowding, the future Commander-in-Chief of Fighter Command. We should be thankful for that and to him in a future battle.

In 1913, Harold having joined the Royal Aeronautical Society, became a test pilot with Vickers after the death of L F Macdonald in a new Vickers monoplane, sadly an all-too-frequent event in the early history of flying. He participated in a number of air races during 1913 and in the following year, on 6 of June, flew a Sopwith Tabloid in the third Aerial Derby. With the onset of the First World War in August 1914 Brooklands closed, and Harold moved to the Vickers airfield at Joyce Green in Kent, testing the Vickers FB5 Gunbus. In 1915 he also found enough spare time to design and build his 'Barnwell Bullet', a high-speed scout (early fighter type aircraft). This was officially recognised and given the Vickers type number ES1. 60 of a developed version the FB19 were produced. While testing a FB11 tractor biplane in August 1916, a defect in its controls caused him to crash land, leading to five weeks in Crayford Hospital. Then tragically, on 25 August 1917, near to where the FB11

crashed, he was killed after failing to recover from a spin while testing the Vickers FB26 prototype. He was 38 years of age. The aircraft had been flown by other pilots that day, including being spun in both directions. The inquest on his death gave the vedict that he had been taken ill at the controls, a view supported by the fact that he did suffer from poor health and had been off ill for the previous fortnight, returning to work just that day.

It was a very sad affair for he was a most talented man, 'much too good for a mere test-pilot', it was said, without much insight to the real nature of test flying then and since. Harold Barnwell had become a most experienced aircraft designer, engineer and pilot. A man of ideas, unassuming, bluff in manner, terse of speech, and a first-class flying instructor, his contribution to aviation, though sadly short, was nevertheless significant.

Meanwhile his brother, Frank, had been making his own way in aviation. In 1909, while still with the Grampian Engineering and Motor Company, he married the daughter of Lieutenant Colonel Charles Sandes of Stirling. It is not clear exactly what his precise role in the business was, though his formal engineering qualifications and his practical experience made him the ideal partner of his brother Harold in their joint aviation activities at Causewayhead. Who did what is open to conjecture however, as both designed and flew, but it would seem that Harold did more of the early flying at Stirling. Like Harold, Frank departed south in December 1911, to join Sir George White's enterprising British & Colonial Aeroplane Company as a designer/draughtsman at Filton, near Bristol, in their experimental, 'secret' department. The previous month, it is said, he had considered investing £2,500 in A V Roe's fledgling firm. The brothers were canny with money; it is thought that they gave up their own aircraft development when it had proved to be a rather expensive business. Then as now!

At Bristol, Frank's job was to assist Lieutenant Charles Burney RN on the latter's novel, but unsuccessful, ideas for sea-launched, hydrofoil/hydropod naval aeroplanes, the X1, 2 and 3.

This experiment came to an end in 1914.

Sir George White, of the Bristol Tramway Company, had been holidaying at Cannes in 1909 and had been impressed by seeing French aviators' experiments, rather like the Barnwells', earlier, and had determined to become involved in aviation. This he did at Filton at a site that is still in use today by BAE SYSTEMS. Filton was the northern terminus of the White's tramway system, and 'Filton House' was soon taken over by his company. It was there that the Brabazon was designed, built and flown in the late 1940s, and Concorde in the late 1960s. It is still a very important place for both airframe and aircraft engine design and manufacture.

In 1912 Frank joined the Royal Aero Club. With Australian Harry Busteed, he created the prototype of the Bristol Scout, a small, single-seater biplane powered by an 80HP Gnome rotary engine. This characterised Frank Barnwell's design philosophy of the smallest airframe with the biggest engine.

It was initially designated SN183 so as to avoid upsetting Bristol's senior designer at the time, the innovative Romanian Henri Coanda. He is best known for the 'Coanda effect', concerned with airflow over a wing.

The Scout 'A' was exibited at the Olympia show in 1914, to some acclaim and achieved a speed of 100.6 mph over a quarter-of-a-mile while being flown by Lord Carberry – an unofficial speed record at the time. Sadly on July 11th, while participating in the London to Paris air race, the Scout 'A' crashed and sank in the Channel.

The Bristol company also had a flying school at Brooklands alongside Vickers, with whom there were good relations. It was in a Bristol Scout 'C' that Major Lanoe Hawker would win his VC on 25 July 1915, after an aerial combat in which he shot down three enemy aircraft.

Frank received his aviator's certificate, No 986, on 9 December 1914 and volunteered for the Royal Flying Corps, becoming a Second Lieutenant. At this time, private companies were having a hard time selling their own-designed aircraft to the military – official policy being to order only those designed by the Royal Aircraft Factory at Farnborough. These were sub-contracted to various firms for manufacture – a matter which exercised the highly critical pen of Charles C Grey of *The Aeroplane* magazine. Needs must and policy must change, particularly so after the appalling losses suffered by the RFC during 1915. However, Farnborough did produce some good fighting machines, like the SE5.

In the winter of 1914, Frank had given a paper to the University of Glasgow Engineering Society on 'Aeroplane Design'. It was subsequently published in *The Aeroplane* 'without any alterations and deletions or amendments' as Grey put it in his introduction to Frank's book *Aeroplane Design*, published in 1917. Frank, in the preface to the book, admits to making a few changes, 'most of small moment'. In addition, this volume contained, 'a simple explanation of inherent stability' by W H Sayers. Thus did Frank follow Percy Pilcher's earlier lectures, the first I suppose to that same society, on aviation. Pilcher's lecture, on 12 December 1895, was also the first to be given in the UK by someone who had actually achieved repeated flights in a heavier-than-air machine. Frank Barnwell was bringing the subject up to date and speaking then as one of our most talented and experienced aircraft designers – less than ten years after his graduation at Gilmorehill.

It has become something of a tradition in what is now the Department of Aerospace Engineering to have the pleasure of repeating that idea, for in 2001, this anniversary year, Dr Henry Macdonald, graduate in aeronautical engineering from the University of Glasgow and presently Director of the NASA Ames Laboratory in the USA, gave the Shoda Lecture – looking to the future with the true conquest of space a real possibility and at a not too dissimilar point in development to that of flying when Frank was speaking in 1914.

Frank, it would seem, was not the best of pilots, but he was an accomplished designer and engineer. Thus, sensibly, in August 1915, now a Captain, he returned to Bristol on indefinite

Frank Barnwell's Bristol M 1c, Turnberry, 1918

leave from the Royal Flying Corps, and without pay. He was given the services of Leslie Frise as his assistant and Clifford Tinson as draughtsman. His time there as aircraft designer and engineer would last until his untimely and tragic death in 1938, just before the outbreak of the Second World War.

What these Scottish brothers began at Balfron and Causewayhead, would lay the foundation on which were built some of Britain's finest flying machines. With Harold's early death in 1917, the creative flame was to be kept burning brightly by brother Frank.

During 1916, a further development of the Scout 'A', the Model D was produced. Frank then designed two very significant aircraft for the Bristol company. First to fly, on 14 July, was the M1, (Type 20), a single-seat monoplane fighter – badly needed. It would have been well used on the Western Front but for the official prejudice against monoplanes generally. Some of these

Frank Barnwell's Bristol F 2B

had, admittedly, suffered a number of structural failures perhaps due to their wing-warping arrangements. The M1's landing speed of 49 mph was also thought 'officially' to be excessive for the fields in France! Those that were ordered, saw service in the Middle East and on training units including the School of Air Fighting at Turnberry. They were popular with their pilots, some as senior officers' hacks. 129 M1s were actually built. Might we see its genesis in the Barnwell monoplane of 1911? One was tried out in France during January 1917; however Trenchard, perhaps in the light of poor experience with Morane-Saulnier Type N monoplane wrote to the Director of Air Organisation on the 23rd of that month, stating that he did not want any more Bristol monoplanes sent to France.

On 9 September 1917 the prototype Bristol F2A/B Fighter, (Type 14/17), made its first flight. This was a two-seat, multi-purpose machine powered by a Rolls-Royce Falcon engine. It was to become the highly successful and much loved 'Brisfit', of which a total of nearly 5500 were built, serving the Royal Air Force until 1932, latterly with the Oxford University Air

Squadron. Some were still flying with the Royal New Zealand Air Force up to 1938.

After the entry into the war by the USA, 'Brisfits' were built there using the Liberty engine. A 'Brisfit' captured the unofficial height record in November 1918.

In 1919 Frank Barnwell was appointed OBE and awarded the AFC for his outstanding efforts. He joined the Royal Aeronautical Society as a Member on 4 March 1914 and was elected a Fellow in December 1917, having served on a Committee considering the Society's future.

In 1920, Frank read a paper to the Cambridge University Aeronautical Society in which he outlined his vision of the future aircraft including the Type 64 which would achieve a speed of 380 mph and require an engine of 3000 hp! The Type 65, on the other hand was to be a human-powered pusher biplane!

With the Armistice, on 11 November 1918, the need for new military aircraft was almost wiped out, and the industry which had grown greatly to meet the exigencies of war faced an uncertain, much-reduced future. In common with others in the industry, Bristol was having a very hard time making ends meet. The next ten years would be very lean indeed, with many types being schemed, some prototypes being built and flown but few orders being received. This was to become a feature of the peacetime British aircraft industry. The military were awash with unwanted aircraft, a few of which were converted for civil use. Civil aviation as such began again in 1919 and Bristol had produced the Type 58/62, an eight-seater passenger/cargo biplane which began experimental services to the continent from Croydon Airport for Handley Page Transport. A later model, the Type 75 Bristol Freight Carrier was operated by Imperial Airways.

However, the opportunities were clearly very limited and, seeking a more productive use of his talents and awaiting a change in the situation at Bristol, Frank went to Australia with his wife and three sons where he received a temporary commission as a Squadron Leader in the Royal Australian Air Force. Along with the Australian Squadron Leader L J Wackett, he might well be regarded as one of the founders of that country's aircraft industry but his time in Australia was not a happy one for he was regarded as just another 'Pommy'. He returned to Bristol in 1923, once more as chief designer, a position he held until 1936 when he became chief engineer. Among the few Bristol production types of the early/mid 1920s were some trainers. The Type 89, which was used by the Beardmore Flying School at Renfew until its closure in 1929, was one. The British aircraft industry, in fact the industry worldwide, engaged much of its energies until well after the Second World War producing far more 'brochures' and prototypes than production aeroplanes.

Leslie Frise became Frank Barnwell's assistant once more, and Clifford Tinson returned from working with Frederick Sage and Company to be his chief draughtsman. The 'Old Man's' team was back in business. That soubriquet was a mixture of respect and affection, and maybe an affectionate reflection of his modest unassuming manner, his thinning hair, and a limp, the result of a crash while in the RFC. The Barnwells set up home in Alveston House, Alveston, Gloucestershire.

In March 1925, a young graduate of the University of Bristol joined Barnwell's team, Archibald E Russell. Such was the progress in aviation during the next fifty years that Russell would become the father of supersonic commercial air travel as one of the principal designers of the aircraft which realised that dream, the Anglo-French Concorde. He would retire in 1969, the year of Concorde's first flight, as Sir Archibald Russell, 'Boss' of what is now British Aircraft Corporation's operations at Filton. Frank would surely have been astonished and quietly pleased. Barnwell's approach to design was a rather solitary one for, with the specification in his hand, he would seclude himself in his office, to reappear a week or two later with a well-worked-out and immaculately presented set of proposals. It has been remarked that he did not seem to have a greatly developed aesthetic sense, or feel for line in his designs, and certainly some of the 1920s Bristol aircraft were rather ungainly, but then so were many others at the time. It is surprising and, I think, unusual for a draughtsman of his ability, for drawing skill is often – even usually – accompanied by aesthetic sensibility. He has also been described as an 'amateur, in the proper sense', but then most in aviation were, necessarily so, in the beginning.

In his splendid autobiography, *Not Much of an Engineer*, the late Sir Stanley Hooker of Rolls- Royce and Bristol Engine Company fame writes of designers: *'The word "engineer" covers a variety of expertises and people of very varying backgrounds. In my experience, the creme de la creme of these are the designers and, if it be true that the status of engineers is too low in Britain, then the charge applies first and foremost to designers.*

'They are enthusiasts, who seek after something more than wealth and power. They lead a tiring and exacting life, standing long hours at their boards drawing, in two dimensions, engine parts that they visualise in their minds in three dimensions.

'They are the "keepers of the trade"', which embodies all the details

of past experience so hardly learned. They are indeed an elite body, yet they are almost always quiet and modest, capable of defending their creation with lucid arguments. At the end of the day, they can look at an engine and say, "I created those parts, and they are exactly as I saw them in my mind when I took a blank sheet of paper, and they work"'

Techniques may change but that reeks of an eternal truth.

The pioneers faced a daunting if exhilarating task. Not only did they have to come to some understanding of the rudimentary notions of aerodynamics together with the problems of constructing the lightest but strongest possible structure from the available materials and similarly in respect of an engine but also, having surmounted those difficulties, they had to find out how to fly their creation, discovering at first hand their handiwork's frailties and foibles. Not for them the old academic adage: 'Never mind if it works practically – does it work in theory?'

Aviation is an ever challenging business in all its aspects and demands the best in courage, creativity and committment from those who engage in it.

Consider the range and scale of the problems faced by the designer of an aircraft or its powerplant where practical solutions are sought at the very edges of the known natural world in a whole host of disciplines in physics and chemistry, fluid dynamics/aerodynamics, mechanics, electronics and materials, all wrapped up neatly in numbers. The resulting product has then to be made manufacturable, has to work well in the most demanding of environments, equally well in the torrid heat of the tropics and in the frozen wastes of the Arctic; at sea-level and near the edge of space; from standing still to faster than sound, in all weathers and atmospheric convulsions safely and securely; in peace and in war and, oh, it has to be capable of being manufactured economically, all the while being subject to and satisfying the most extensive and rigorous regulatory regime known, and – I nearly forgot – make a profit for its makers.

This was not an enterprise for the fainthearted a hundred years ago, and it is assuredly not one now.

This country takes its engineers for granted while feting such as footballers and pop stars. It is engineers who make our world and keep it going, yet even such great engineers as Sir Nigel Gresley, Chief Mechanical Engineer of the LNER and responsible for some of our most successful railway locomotives and rolling stock – the 'Silver Jubilee' and 'Coronation' expresses of the pre-war era, – isn't recorded, yet, in the *Dictionary of National Biography*: nor were Cayley or Stringfellow – a matter raised by Walter Raleigh in *The War in the Air*.

Civilisation owes so much to engineers and engineering, despite Robert Burns' expressed disgust after visiting the Carron Ironworks in 1787:

> *We cam na here to view your warks,*
> *In hopes to be mair wise,*
> *But only, lest we gang to Hell,*
> *It may be nae surprise.*

' human kind differs from all other life by its ability to imagine and create. This is an ability greater than that of analysis by science or sensory stimulation by art. Not merely because it needs both of these to create something greater but because in doing so it provides for our fellow men.'

Lord Baker OBE FRS FEng in *An Engineer's Message*

Leslie Frise, Frank Barnwell's assistant, would also make a most notable contribution to aircraft design for well over fifty years, including designing the 'Frise' aileron, as a way round an existing patent, a not unusual situation and spur to creativity. After thirty-two years at Bristol he left in 1948, reportedly frustrated at the stultifying stranglehold still exercised by the ruling families there, to go to the Percival Aircraft Company at Luton where he produced a number of well-known aircraft such as the Prince, the Provost, and the Jet Provost. In 1956 he went to Blackburn Aircraft as Director of Special Projects, retiring in 1962 and forming his own companies, Frise Patents and Frise Enterprises

Ltd. This remarkable man died, almost unknown and unrecognised, on 26 September 1979 at his home at Clifton, near Brunel's great supension bridge. His way of working was quite different to that of Frank Barnwell, for he involved his staff in more open discussion.

Back at Bristol, the talented and innovative engine designer Roy Fedden became a valued part of the team when the Cosmos Engine Company, which had taken over Fedden's 1917 Brazil Straker company, itself became part of what had become, on 31 December 1919, the Bristol Aeroplane Company. Thus airframe and engine design and manufacture came together, a good thing for Bristol's given the difficult prevailing economic circumstances, but also good in that airframe and engine combinations would be mutually, and advantagously developed. This arrangement would stand well until the drastic reshaping and rationalisations of the British aircraft industry during the 1960s. That era might well be remembered as much for the public money wasted in 'projects cancelled' by government as for its real successes.

In early 1925, Richard Fairey astounded the aviation world with his sleek silver Fox, a biplane day-bomber, powered by a Curtiss D12 in-line engine, enabling it to easily out perform the service fighters of the day, such as the Armstrong Whitworth Siskin and Gloster Gamecock. Its performance was largely due to its slim, liquid-cooled in-line engine. Roy Fedden on the other hand was a convinced air-cooled, radial man, a configuration the Bristol Engine Company used throughout its existence for its piston powerplans, and with much success. Hugh Trenchard, Chief of Air Staff, immediately bought a squadron of Foxes to equip 12 Squadron, Frank's old RFC unit, giving them the nickname thereafter of 'Shiny Twelve', from their polished cowlings.

Also in 1925, the Air Ministry sponsored a 'Light Aeroplane' competition and Bristol's fielded the Type 91, a low-wing monoplane powered by a 24 hp Bristol Cherub. Flown by Cyril Uwins, it came second to the Beardmore 'Wee Bee'. Shades of a future tragedy...

The need for a new fighter was evident and the official specification, F9/26, for a day and night fighter was issued. A previous proposal by Barnwell for a fighter aircraft had been rejected and it would seem that Frise decided to 'do his own thing'. 'It was a move which needed delicate handling, for he was virtually going behind the back of Barnwell to whom he had no wish to be disloyal.' It was remarked that Frise, like Fedden, was possessed of great determination and an unwillingness to accept failure. Both were instrumental in saving the company in difficult times. At any rate Frise was allowed to proceed with two designs, the Types 105 (F9/26) and the smaller 107 (F17/24). It might be said that both had their origins in Barnwell's earlier Types 101 and 102. It says much about Frank Barnwell as a man that this affair did not seem to injure his relationship with Frise for they continued to work well together.

A E Russell did much of the stress calculation, laying in the groundwork perhaps, for his future supersonic success! The Type 105 became the famous 'Bulldog' fighter of the Royal Air Force between the Wars – 501 being built. There is a hint of Harold Barnwell's Vicker's 'Bullet' in its shape.

The Type 130 of 1933 became the 'Bombay', a high-wing, twin-engined transport carrying up to twenty-four armed troops. This was produced in some quantity and served the RAF up to and during the Second World War.

Other notable aircraft from the Bristol stable were the Type 110A, a light passenger aircraft and the Type 138A which, between 1928 and 1937, broke the world altitude record nine times. This was powered by a Bristol Pegasus, also used by the Westland aircraft, in which those two intrepid Scottish Auxiliary Air Force aviators, the Marquess of Douglas and Clydesdale and David F McIntyre, achieved their epic Everest flight in 1933. They were successive COs of 602 (City of Glasgow) Squadron Auxiliary, later, Royal Auxiliary Air Force, the first such squadron to be formed, on 12 September 1925, at Renfrew – one of Trenchard's most inspired creations.

In 1934 however, an advanced, low-wing, twin-engined passenger aircraft with Bristol Aquila engines was designed, the

Hawker Hart of 602 Squadron over the Clyde, 1935 with an Avro 504N

Type 135. It was called 'The Captain's Gig'. To be of much more future significance was an even sleeker twin, the Type 142 of 1935, built to the requirements of the newspaper baron and 'apostle of air power', Lord Rothermere, once again involved in the politics of aviation as he sought to alert and awaken the British establishment to the growing threats facing the nation and to demonstrate the obsolecence of much of the contemporary RAF's equipment. This machine, dubbed 'Britain First', ostensibly a kind of executive aircraft of its day, outclassed the military machines. That was not to last for from it was developed a military version, Barnwell's famous Blenheim light bomber. Despite being ahead of its time initially, it was becoming obsolescent when the conflict actually came. Nonetheless, it served throughout the Second World War in all theatres and in many roles. Rothermere was still at it as late as 1950 when, against a rumoured threat to abolish Bomber Command, he spoke at the Pathfinder Association Dinner in May of that year saying: 'If politicians tried to abolish Bomber Command they would have a menace on their hands greater than the Russian threat.'

Tragically, all three sons of Frank and Marjorie Barnwell were killed in the air during the Second World War while on active service, two of them in Blenheims.

Frank Barnwell himself was killed in the crash of the 'Barnwell weekender', a little aircraft he had designed and built for himself privately, away from the factory and officialdom. He had been banned from piloting by the company, as being uninsurable. Refusing all assistance, even from Bristol's great test pilot, Cyril Uwins, he made one successful flight but during the second, on 2 August 1938, the aircraft stalled and spun-in, killing him. He was 58, a designer, engineer and great Scottish gentleman who contributed much to our progress in aviation. He was possessed of great patience in the face of an often, as he saw it, stultifying bureaucracy, once being heard to say quietly: 'We struggle against a sea of fools'. Many of us in education can sympathise with him! He lies with his wife Marjorie in Saint Helen's Churchyard, Alveston, South Gloucester.

In the discussion after the first Royal Aeronautical Society's 'Barnwell Memorial Lecture', given by a former colleague, Major G P Bulman on 4 March 1954, in the presence of a number of Frank's close associates, Clifford Tinson, his early assistant commented: '*He was a grand man – and a great one, for we must not forget that the industrial prosperity of a city is largely bound up with the deeds and accomplishments of men among whom Barnwell must be numbered*'. Leslie Frise observed: '*He had a flair for aircraft design,*

although our knowledge was ridiculously small then that one sometimes wonders that things ever worked at all'.

May we remember Frank Barnwell and his brother Harold.

The Blenheim paved the way for the Beaufort torpedo bomber, in which Kenneth Campbell from Saltcoats won a posthumous VC for his 'suicidal' attack on Brest harbour, and then the splendid Beaufighter, well named the 'Whispering Death' for the smooth quietness of its Bristol Hercules sleeve-valve engines. It would serve with distinction in many capacities during the Second World War, ending its days in the mid 1950s, target-towing. One was recently repatriated from South Africa to the Museum of Flight at East Fortune where it will be displayed statically after restoration, a worthy addition to Scotland's aircraft collection.

It is really sad, however, that so much of Scotland's proud industrial past, in the form of the artefacts we designed and made for the world, has been allowed to disappear for ever. In this respect the Heritage Lottery Fund has been a disappointment. We need to address this issue and the once touted notion of a 'Scottish Industrial Museum', as per 'The Museum of Scotland', should be brought to fruition soon, and in the West of Scotland.

After the Second World War, the Bristol company, went on to produce a few notable aircraft, the huge Brabazon, ambitious, but too potentially uneconomic; the quiet, 'whispering giant', Britannia, turboprop transatlantic transport potentially successful but too late and thus overtaken by the coming of the big jets in the late 1950s. These Bristol aircraft were maybe the origins of our supersonic ambitions which were to be realised in the superb Anglo-French Concorde – in many ways a Bristol product! The Bristol Aeroplane Company became 20% of the British Aircraft Corporation in 1960, and after further rationalisation, a part of today's BAE SYSTEMS. Archibald Russell, who had been taken on by Frank Barnwell in 1925, and eventually became his successor as chief designer after Leslie Frise, might well entitle his autobiography *A Span of Wings*. Tribute should

'The Art of Engineering'. The Rolls-Royce 'Tay' Turbofan
developed from the 'Spey' at Rolls-Royce, East Kilbride. Sandy MacFarlane and Norman Welers to the fore

also be made to Dr W J (Bill) Strang for much of the later Bristol aircraft including some significant but stillborn projects and for a major contribution to the design of Concorde.

With the rationalisation of the 1960s together with the end of the remaining ruling family dynasties, the nationalisation of the aircraft and shipbuilding industries in the 1970s, followed by pri-

vatisation in the 1980s, it might be wondered how these important industries managed to produce anything other than paper policies and strategies. That the aircraft industry has done so, and continues to do so, and makes, yes, makes a very significant contribution to our economy both internally and in export terms is to the everlasting credit of those engaged in its business.

The decision in 1997 to close the Jetstream 41 line at

Prestwick, (104 of which had been completed), brought fifty years of designing, building and testing complete commercial aircraft in Scotland to an end. Nearly one thousand aircraft had been made – from the 'Prestwick Pioneer' of 1947 to the 'Jetstream 41' via the 'Twin Pioneer', 'Bulldog' and 'Jetstream T1/ 2, 31/32'.

In 1995, when the first of the present series of Pilcher Lectures was presented, Scotland could boast of designing and building commercial aircraft for the world – through British Aerospace at Prestwick and Rolls-Royce at East Kilbride.

The cancellation by BAE SYSTEMS of its last major indigenous civil aircraft programme, the RJX development of the 146, Regional jet, in December 2001, brings to an end UK civil transport aircraft development. With it, once again, goes a whole set of technologies and the knowledge and experience of design, manufacturing, testing and marketing of complete civil aircraft, just another major business abandoned, another to join a dismal list. Fortunately, the whole residual regional aircraft engineering functions have been transferred to Prestwick thus maintaining a significant engineering capability there.

One hundred years on from the Wrights' triumph, the UK does have genuine world-class abilities in aviation in a few areas – aero-engines (Rolls-Royce); wing design and manufacture (for Airbus by BAE SYSTEMS); in avionics (BAE SYSTEMS and Smiths Aerospace); and in ejector seats (Martin Baker); also in overhaul and modification (Marshalls), but it is a far cry from the plethora of companies founded before, and built up during, the Second World War, during the first half-century of flight.

Scottish Aviation Ltd at Prestwick – initially running a reserve flying school in association with De Havillands – had built up a considerable expertise in airframe and engine overhaul, modification and design after the Second World War, marketing this as 'Salcheck' during the 1960s. This was abandoned after nationalisation though there is currently a growing design activity at BAE SYSTEMS for some of the big global players. The aerostructures business however is presently (mid 2003) up

for sale. We can hope that the quality work which has been SAL's and BAE's hallmark will be taken over as a going concern – by a Scottish company perhaps – and be regenerated. Is there the much needed political will and understanding? How have we allowed our industry to be so easily outmanoeuvered by our European competitors, as much as those in emerging economies?

On a more optimistic front, even if whole commercial aircraft are no longer being designed and made either in Scotland or the UK, there is an increasing effort and activity in sub-contract aerospace work in both design and manufacture at Prestwick and in aero engines – East Kilbride Engineering Services, and in avionics – BAE SYSTEMS (formerly Marconi, originally Ferranti). An airpark is being developed at Prestwick which bodes well for the future. Polar Air has built a fine facility for the maintenance of Boeing 747s. BAE SYSTEMS employed around 150 engineers when the J41 programme was cancelled in 1997. In 2002 it is employing around 270 and looks to having more in the future as design and other regional aircraft engineering and service functions are brought to Prestwick. No visitor can fail to be impressed by the capability, capacity and enthusiasm found there. This is a significant concentration of intellectual capital. It may be then that in the global aerospace business there is a place for that peculiar Scottish genius for creative engineering which our education system still nurtures and produces. It needs, as does our society, to recognise the vital role which eccentricity and enthusiasm coupled to the curiosity of enquiring minds play in a healthy society, with the pursuit of excellence for its own inspiring sake. Can, will, our reconvened Parliament rise to the challenges and opportunities presenting themselves to Scotland and its people and play its part?

So far as making is concerned, there are four basic means available using either natural or synthetic materials. We can carve it out of the solid. We can cast it. We can fabricate it or we can accept it raw from nature itself.

Making things for our use and delight is an inescapable

Aeroplane at Monkton, July 1913. Where Prestwick Airport now is

A Pioneer demonstrating it's short take-off, 1953

Scottish Aviation's 'Prestwick' Pioneers for the Royal Malayan Air Force, 1962

A line-up of Twin Pioneers in 1958 and below: Scottish Aviation's first venture into helicopters, one of the Bell 47s at Prestwick 1947

A Pioneer in Malaya where it's short take-off and landing capabilities were used to great effect. Below, a Twin Pioneer in RAF service

Bulldog productuion line at Scottish Aviation in 1971

End of the line? The last production aircraft designed and built in Scotland – Jetstream 41 for the Hong Kong Government with the Pioneer Flying Group's Bulldog and a company J31

Bulldogs of the Universities of Glasgow and Strathclyde Air Squadron over Glasgow University

human necessity and answers a basic human creative urge. No longer just for bare survival, we engage in it to satisfy our increasingly sophisticated tastes and lifestyles. There are but three ways of satisfying our needs. We can grow it, (the Agrarian revolution). We can mine it or we can make it (the Industrial Revolution). This country has to use its creative and intellectual skills to be smart in making money from making things.

The rate of technological change during the century has driven the aviation industry to great achievements and innovations. From its innovative technologies many spin-offs have found their way into our ordinary lives. And there are still examples of heroic engineering equal to those of our forefathers – the Channel Tunnel, the whole business of extracting oil from the North Sea and our first steps into the conquest of space, for example.

What Pilcher, the Barnwells, Dickson, Henderson and so many other Scots among the great global company of aviators began and the courage and skills they so amply displayed during the first century of powered flight, is needed more than ever today. I have no doubt that today's young people are well up to the job; are the rest of us?

This essay is dedicated to all those men and women of creative genius whose courage, commitment, imagination and ingenuity created a great industry and to those, especially those, who carry it on today. They demonstrated, and their successors can still demonstrate, these characteristics to the full, despite much discouragement. The great art of engineering is our birthright. Let us not fail to claim it, for the future will need it even more than the past!

Dugald Cameron

Pastiche of civil aircraft in 1934 at Renfrew Airport

[They]
Travelled a short way towards the sun
And left the vivid air signed with their honour
Stephen Spender

The story of the Department of Aerospace Engineering and its part in this adventure, is also one of which we in the City of Glasgow can be proud.

The aviation story really began with ballooning, and 'home-building'. Both are alive and well in the 21st century, as sporting

and recreational activities. Don Cameron, a former pupil of the late and lamented Allan Glen's school, that Glaswegian seed bed of scientists and engineers, a graduate of the University of Glasgow in aeronautical engineering and a former member of the Air Squadron, has built a successful business designing and making balloons for commercial and other purposes, based in Bristol. He himself is a record-breaking balloonist. In July 2002, the American balloonist Steve Fosset became the first person to circumnavigate the world solo in a balloon designed and built by Don Cameron. Cameron himself at this time was preparing to go for the altitude record. Mike Timmons is a graduate of the University of Glasgow both in Aeronautical Engineering and in Medicine and is a home-builder of light aircraft – his advanced glass fibre and foam Rutan 'Long-eze' G-OMJT is a notable design. Its canard

foreplanes use an aerofoil section the GU25 designed at the University of Glasgow by the late Professor Terence Nonweiler. Bob McKinlay, was a senior engineering manager on Concorde and, like Frank Barnwell, he studied at the Royal College of Science and Technology (previously the Glasgow and West College) and graduated from the University of Glasgow. He has also delivered the Pilcher lecture when he addressed the subject of future supersonic transport aircraft.

The late Charles Oakley both studied and lectured (in management) at the University of Glasgow and, echoing William Weir's activities during the First World War, he was the Air

Mike Timmons' home built, Rutan 'Long-eze'

Ministry's Controller of Aircraft Production in Scotland during the Second World War.

In terms of administrative contribution to early aviation, J D Cormack was appointed Professor of Civil Engineering and Mechanics at the University of Glasgow in 1913, and holder of the Rankine Chair, founded by Queen Victoria in 1840. He became Chief Contracts Officer of Military Aeronautics in 1915 and subsequently Director of Aircraft Supply and Equipment, returning to his Chair in 1919. He was responsible for bringing Alexander Thom to Glasgow in 1921 to teach a sixty-lecture course in aeronautics. Thom had been designing for De Havilland among others. His son Archie was to play an important role in the Department of Aeronautical Engineering as Roddy Galbraith will tell.

ACKNOWLEDGMENTS

THE AUTHORS are most grateful to the University of Glasgow, its Principal and Vice-Chancellor Sir Graeme Davies for his support and to the Faculty of Engineering. To the W M Mann Foundation, through Mr Billy Mann, for their most generous assistance in providing the initial private funding for this project and to Stephen Baxter, BAA Glasgow: Scott Grier, Loganair and The Hugh Fraser Foundation and Dr Kenneth Chrystie for their enthusiastic assistance and financial contributions which have made possible the publication of the original lecture in this greatly extended form.

Also to Lord James Douglas Hamilton for his introduction and to James W Murray for designing the publication.

Our gratitude goes to the Royal Aeronautical Society Library and the Royal Air Force Museum for their permission to reproduce photographs from their collections of Henderson and Barnwell and to *The Herald* newspaper. Others have been used whose owners are unknown. We trust that they will understand and approve.

We are also indebted to Kate Blackadder for her care in editing the manuscript.

Dugald Cameron was formerly Director of Glasgow School of Art and is presently a Visiting Professor to the Department of Aerospace Engineering at the University of Glasgow, and in Product Design at the University of Strathclyde. He is Patron of the Universities of Glasgow and Strathclyde Air Squadron.

Roderick A McD Galbraith is Shoda Professor of Aerospace Engineering at the University of Glasgow. He was a co-recipient of the Royal Aeronautical Society's Edward Busk Memorial Prize in 2001.

Dr Douglas Thomson is Head of the Department of Aerospace Engineering at the University of Glasgow.

I am particularly indebted to Dr K J H Mackay of Cambusbarron for giving free access to his research on the Barnwells and to Philip Jarrett, as always, for his friendship, patience and generous assistance on early aviation generally: his help was invaluable; to Ray Sturtivant for his unfailing assistance as always, and to Alan Carlaw for scanning the illustrations.

Also to Lyell Munro MBE (Mil) via James Munro, for allowing me access to his work on Bertram Dickson; Dr Neil Geddes; Dougal McIntyre; Margaret Morrell; and colleagues in the University of Glasgow – Professor Roddy Galbraith, Dr Douglas Thomson in the Department of Aerospace Engineering and to Emeritus Professor Hugh Sutherland for his various insights into the University of Glasgow matters. The opinions expressed are those of the authors alone.

BIBLIOGRAPHY AND SOURCES CONSULTED

University of Glasgow, Archives
University of Strathclyde, Archives
Fettes College, Archives
Mitchell Library, Glasgow
Royal Society, Library
Royal Aeronautical Society, Library
Air Historical Branch, MoD, Sebastian Cox

Books

Sir Frederick Sykes and the Air Revolution 1912-1918 Eric Ash (Frank Cass)
Bristol Aircraft C H Barnes (Putnam)
The Aeroplanes of the Royal Flying Corps Military Wing J M Bruce (Putnam)
Cierva Autogyros Peter W Brooks (Smithsonian)
Birth of Military Aviation1903-1914 Hugh Driver Royal (Historical Society and The Boydell Press)
Aviation – a historical survey Charles H Gibbs-Smith (HMSO)
Sir George Cayley's Aeronautics Charles H Gibbs-Smith (HMSO)
The Wright Brothers Charles H Gibbs-Smith (HMSO)
A Brief History of Flying Charles H Gibbs-Smith (HMSO)
The Rebirth of European Aviation Charles H Gibbs-Smith (Science Museum and HMSO)
Brief Preliminary Notes on the Aircraft Designed and Constructed by the late Preston Watson Charles H Gibbs-Smith 1957 (unpublished)
Aviation in Scotland Gillies and Wood (Royal Aeronautical Society, Glasgow Branch)
Not Much of an Engineer Sir Stanley Hooker (Airlife)
Jan Christian Smuts Kenneth Ingham (Weidenfeld and Nicholson)
Another Icarus Philip Jarrett (Smithsonian)
Pioneer Aircraft edited by Philip Jarrett (Putnam)

Bulldog David Luff (Airlife)
High Commanders of the Royal Air Force Henry Probert (HMSO)
Lion Rampant and Winged Alan Robertson (privately published)
Air Power and the Royal Navy Geoffrey Till (Janes Publishing)
Walking in all the Squares Archibald S Thom (Argyll Publishing)
War in the Air Sir Walter Raleigh and H A Jones (Oxford University Press)

Journals

Cross and Cockade Vol 32/3and 4
Forgotten Founder Francois Prins (Air Enthusiast No 47)
Air Power and Imperial Defence Michael Purvis (Journal of Contemporary History,Vol. 24/2)
First Barnwell Memorial Lecture 1954 (Journal of the Royal Aeronautical Society)
Scots Magazine

As a personal postscript, may I add another anniversary in 2003 – the fiftieth anniversary of the establishment of the 'Prestwick Spotter's Club' by a group of young aircraft enthusiasts at Prestwick Airport in October 1953, led by that doughty champion of Prestwick, David Reid. This is still very active and includes in its Alumni many who have gone on to occupy senior positions in the world aviation industry and leadership in military aviation. I am proud to have been one of the original members who met firstly in the public enclosure and then by the kindess of the airport authorities, in the clubhouse they provided.

As I write this in the summer of 2002, David Reid and that other stalwart Wilf White, the photographer to whom we all are grateful for his remarkable collection, are still, in their eighties, active enthusiasts – there is a moral there.

Dugald Cameron 2003

Flight

How can they know that joy to be alive who have not flown
To loop and spin and roll and climb and dive, the very sky one's own,
The urge of power while engines race, the sting of speed,
The rude winds, buffet on one's face, to live indeed.

How can they know the grandeur of the sky, the earth below,
The restless sea, and waves that break and die with ceaseless ebb and flow;
The morning sun on drifting clouds and rolling downs –
and valley mists that shroud the chimneyed towns

So long has puny man to earth been chained who now is free,
And with this conquest of the air has gained a glorious liberty.
How splendid is this gift He gave on high to roam,
The sun a friend, the earth a slave, the heavens home.

Brian Young, Cranwell 1938

A TOPICAL HISTORY OF THE DEPARTMENT OF AEROSPACE ENGINEERING, UNIVERSITY OF GLASGOW

Roderick A McD Galbraith

The Beginning

ALTHOUGH PILCHER had started an interest in flight within the University during the mid 1890s, formal courses in Aeronautics started in 1921 when Alexander Thom delivered them from the Civil Engineering Department. Some of the early examinations are as relevant today as they were in those early formative days of aerospace development. Thom went on to become the Professor of Engineering Science at Oxford and is noted for two major scientific contributions. First, was the early

development of numerical techniques for assessing the suitability of structures and components to withstand the anticipated maximum forces that would be applied during their 'safe life'; second, to archaeology, for his surveys of standing stones and consequent analysis. His son Archie followed in his footsteps, at Glasgow, to become a senior lecturer in the Aeronautics and Fluid Mechanics Department. Much later, in 1947, a local engineering firm, Mechans Limited of Scotstoun, endowed a Chair at the University. The terms of the University's ordinance were such that the University Court, on the occasion of each appointment, determines the branch of engineering science to which the Professor is responsible. It is to the great credit of the University that they

Professor Alexander Thom

decided to establish what remains the only Department of Aeronautics and Fluid Mechanics (Aerospace Engineering) in Scotland. So in 1950 the Faculty was pleased to welcome Professor William Jolly Duncan to his first meeting, and one year later established the degree of BSc. in Aeronautics.

Professor Duncan (then DSc, FRS) was a man of considerable stature and among those who knew him was held in the very highest regard. He was a native of Glasgow, educated at Allan Glen's School and Dulwich College before graduating at University College of London. His early professional life was at his father's marine engineering firm in Govan. In 1926 he moved to the National Physical laboratories (NPL) at Teddington, where his immediate superior was R . Frazer, a formidable applied mathematician having been Senior Wrangler at Cambridge.

Duncan was recognised immediately as an exceptional experimental scientist imbued with considerable physical insight, but (quoting Collar)

Professor W J Duncan,1960

'His analytical ability, fired undoubtedly by Frazer, soon matched his experimental capabilities'. In 1928, Frazer and Duncan produced *The Flutter of Aeroplane Wings* (ARC Monograph R&M 1155). This document was so authoritative that it became known as 'The Flutter Bible', and even to this

Professor Duncan's Flutter Engine

day is a valuable source of reference in the field. For his considerable contribution to Aerospace he was invited to become the Wakefield Professor at University College, London, and subsequently spent most of the Second World War at the Royal Aircraft Establishment at Farnborough. From there he took up the Chair of Aerodynamics at Cranfield in 1945.

Following the recruitment of Collar in 1930, Collar and Duncan produced, in 1931, their paper 'Resistance Derivatives of Flutter Theory' – the first complete analytical potential flow solution of the problem – some three years ahead of their closest rival, Theodorsen. However, it was by the publication (CUP 1938) of the book *Elementary Matrices* by Frazer, Duncan & Collar – the very first text in which Matrices were treated as a branch of Applied Mathematics – that Duncan's claim to fame was sealed. The book has been reprinted in the UK no fewer

than nine times and there have been several translations into other languages.

For his brilliant research into problems of aircraft stability and control, and his many other achievements, Professor Duncan was elected a Fellow of the Royal Society in 1947. He was recognised as one of the leading aeronautical engineers and chaired the Aeronautical Research Council. Among his other activities, he was the British representative assessing the German aerospace war effort, involved in the Comet enquiry and he invented the flutter engine. That last activity produced an invention to demonstrate that, when an aerofoil flutters, the surrounding air does work on the wing rather than, in normal flight, the wing doing work on the surrounding air.

In 1951 Dr Arthur W Babister was appointed to the Department and he became internationally recognised for the text *Stability and Control*. It was a major contribution and remains the 'Gray's Anatomy' of that discipline.

It was Professor Duncan who wanted the Department to be called 'Aeronautics and Fluid Mechanics' in the belief that, in those days, there would be too few students for Aeronautics alone; typical numbers of yearly graduates averaged around four during the 50s and between five and six in the 60s. To bolster the Fluids teaching, Dr Archie S Thom was appointed to the Department in 1952; a civil engineer by training, with Hydraulics as his main discipline. He did some remarkable work with a River Clyde Estuary model and, with Tom Forde, from the department of Civil Engineering, developed the method for monitoring the thermodynamic efficiency of the Dinorwic pump storage scheme turbines in North Wales.

Now these were good days, a handful of students (approximately 19) and no word-processors but, nonetheless, with contemporary similarities. In 1939 Professor Gilbert Cook asked Dr Macdonald to prepare a brief on modernising the hydraulics laboratory. Nothing was done because of the war years. In 1948 he asked Archie Thom to look into the matter but again nothing was done. The latter inactivity may have been due to the immiment arrival of Professor Duncan. On 21 January 1952, however, after frustration with unnecessary delays, Professor Duncan wrote a precise letter to the Court and enclosed a quotation for the work. This was accepted on 11 February 1952.

The Department was fortunate to accept, in 1953, an outstanding aeronautical engineer and perfect gentleman, Tom Cain, bringing the total number of staff to four. Tom's drafting abilities were not only meticulous, but of the highest standard; he was an outstanding designer. His most notable contribution was the design and development of a test facility for assessing the aerodynamic stability of bridges, the last of which was that built over the River Kessock near Inverness.

The Department continued to develop with the appointment of Phil Tanner in 1955, a specialist in Fluid Mechanics. He bolstered up that part of the Department to ease the large service-teaching load. The Department continued to develop with two further appointments: one in 1957, Henry Y Wong, and in 1960 Fred Kelling, bringing the total complement of staff to seven. Both Henry and Fred went on to make very significant contributions to Heat Transfer, suppression of vortex-excited oscillations (most noticeable on the Edinburgh Royal Infirmary chimneys) and the Glasgow-Aerofoil tests, respectively.

Sadly, 1961 was the year of Professor Duncan's death. By all accounts he was a laconic man from whom many people would seek council and advice. Should you desire such council you would simply ask for whatever length of time you required and you got precisely that. At the end of the consultation you would be told, yes, no, or develop that a little more. One interesting incident involved Henry Wong. After his allotted time explaining what he wished to do, Professor Duncan asked, 'How much?' and was told (by today's prices) 'about £200,000'. 'Thank you,' said Professor Duncan, and in the afternoon a copy of a letter arrived containing words to the effect: 'Wong has had a good idea, it will cost £200,000, I am sure that will be okay, William Jolly Duncan' What wonderful esteem and influence.

Kessock Bridge work in the Handley Page wind tunnel

When Professor Duncan died it was a loss to the entire aerospace community. Such was the prestige of the Mechan Chair, however, that the next incumbent, was another towering scholar but, unlike Duncan, an eloquent voluble individual.

Terence R F Nonweiler was born in London in 1925 and educated at Goudhurst, Kent, then graduated BSc Honours in Maths from Manchester in 1944 after which he was with the Royal Aircraft Establishment until 1950 working primarily on high speed aircraft. Later in 1950 he became Scientific Adviser to the Air Ministry and then lectured at Cranfield until 1957 when he went to Queens University in Belfast. His ability had a depth that is rarely seen. The story is told that the secretary said to him, just prior to Christmas, that he really should write up his work and get a PhD. Three weeks later he handed her the first and final written draft, in meticulous copperplate writing. Those who have written a PhD dissertation will recognise that

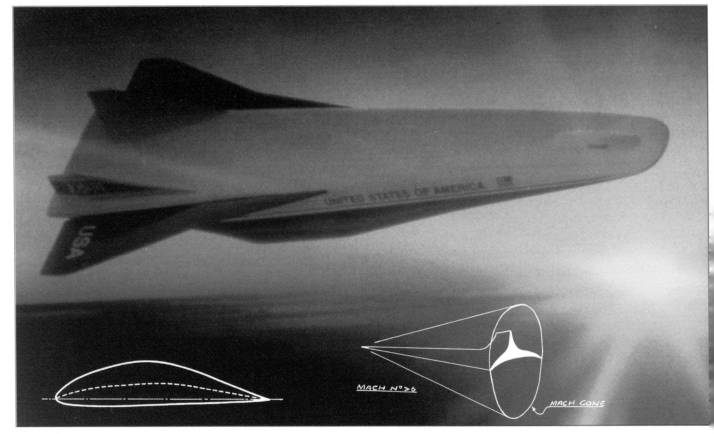

MACH N°>6

MACH CONE

Diagram of one of Glasgow University's many Aerofoils
GU25 was used for the Canard of the Rutan 'Long-eze'

The Waverider and a diagram of it's mach cone

as a remarkable achievement. He was known for many things, including the re-entry of satellites and man-powered aircraft, for which he won the Edward Busk Memorial Prize from the Royal Aeronautical Society. He designed high performance, low-drag aerofoils (wind tunnel tested by Fred Kelling) that have been used on many micro-light aircraft.

In an aside at the end of an exceptionally short paper he proposed an application of the work in the form of a hypersonic craft called a Wave Rider. That became the invention for which he won the Royal Aeronautical Society's Gold Medal and initiated a new field of research. The aircraft rides its own shock wave and, although early interest in it flagged, it was renewed through NASA proposing its use for aero-assisted sling shots past other solar masses.

There were many stories about Terence but one in particular is rather amusing. He had left Professors' Square to walk eastwards over the brow of the hill and down to the Engineering Faculty at the east end of the Campus. It was into the teeth of an easterly gale and Terence was trying, unsuccessfully, to light his pipe. Finally he turned his back to the wind, lifted up his collar, lit his pipe, and ended back where he started, at Professors' Square.

The Wilderness Years

During 1963, David Pirie was welcomed onto the staff, bringing the total number to eight: another quiet gentleman who put students first at all times. The Department then went its merry way until Professor Nonweiler left in 1975. His last appointment was Roderick Galbraith. There was no replacement for Terence and it was only by the good nature and efforts of Archie Thom that the Department survived.

Polarisation had occurred into a dry (aerodynamics) and a wet end (hydraulics); dry on the top floor of the building and wet on the bottom. The Department was slowly approaching its research nadir. Only three of the academics could be said to be research active and only two were producing publications for quality aeronautical journals.

Ironically, student numbers were rising rapidly, but without an equivalent increase in resources. This is hardly surprising when one realises that Archie Thom thought it impolite to ask what budget the Department had been allocated. Even with the increased number of undergraduate students, the Department was drifting. There were no research students, nor could we offer any a place; a consequence of the Department's uncertain future. Part of the reason was that Acting Heads (as Archie was) could not carry the same clout as full Heads, and that left the Department vulnerable. In fact, at the first meeting of the Academic Development Committee 1978, the main agendum was to consider whether or not to close the Department of Aeronautics and Fluid Mechanics: fortunately the decision was no.

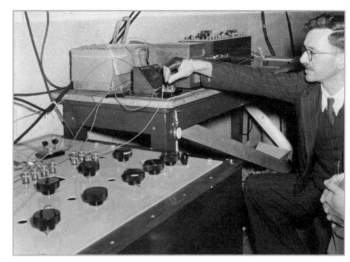

Dr Archie Thom

So at this juncture, with only two staff fully research active, there came, in January 1980, a white knight from Brussels in the form of Professor Bryan E Richards (the third holder of the Mechan Chair). There is no doubt that he saved the Department. 1980 was also the year that Henry Wong was promoted to Professor.

Professor Richards had formerly been head of the High Speed Laboratory in the von Karman Institute, Brussels. He graduated from Queen Mary College in 1960 and worked for two years at the British Aircraft Corporation, Filton, after which he returned to London and Imperial College gaining a PhD in 1967.

The Renaissance

The Department Professor Richards headed was in bad shape with a plethora of obsolete research rigs, never to be reused. Professor Richards was, however, a breath of fresh air and, if the normal constraints and influences on the Department had been

Professor Bryan E Richards

removed, he would have developed the Department further than he managed. The staff could look forward to increasing student numbers, offering research to students once again, and to stable research.

To a great extent the Handley Page wind tunnel had been underused since its arrival in the Department in 1970. It contained 7' x 5' octagonal working section and with a maximum speed of 200 feet per second. The tunnel was an excellent research facility in which Roderick Galbraith and Gordon Leishman (research student) built, with technical support from Richard Gordon (research technologist), Tony Smedley (tunnel technician) and Effie Murray-Smith (computer support), the first low-speed dynamic-stall facility in a British university.

Resources were such, that much of the equipment was begged, borrowed or salvaged from elsewhere. The Department designed its own electronics, rig supports, models and computer software. To a great extent this facility kick-started a new research era in which the previous culture was changed from predominantly individualistic activity to continuity through research teams. The dynamic-stall facility and its spin-offs into wind energy and blade-vortex interaction, brought in millions of pounds of research funding.

Dynamic stall and blade-vortex-interaction are primarily associated with helicopters and this lead to the development of a helicopter flight-dynamics group. Professor Richards in turn got to grips with the rapidly developing field of computational fluid dynamics. These were the initial three kernels of the modern Department and they are still vibrant today together with

*Gordon Leishman in the Handley Page Wind Tunnel
during the first dynamic stall experiments*

space-flight dynamics, flow control, aircraft management, industrial aerodynamics, structures and design.

By 1989 the Department had (by research assessment exercise definition) 35% active staff. The underlying trend, however, was upwards – albeit limited resources and obsolete infrastructure inhibited the Department, like many others.

It was a time of rapid change. Both Arthur Babister and Archie Thom retired in 1979 to be replaced, in part, by Alasdair Caldwell in 1981. In 1983 Phil Tanner retired, and Colin Goodchild, who would develop methodologies for implementing the schemes for Future Air Navigation, known as Free Flight and autonomous aircraft operations, was appointed. In 1985 Ladislav Smrcek, an aircraft designer, and in 1986 John Anderson, a scholar, were appointed. Also in 1986, Alastair Caldwell left for the United States and Henry Wong retired. In 1987 Roy Bradley, helicopter flight dynamicist, was appointed and Roderick Galbraith promoted to Senior Lecturer (the first in the Department for many years). In 1988 Marco Vezza was appointed and David Pirie took early retirement but stayed on, working part-time. Finally, in 1989 Frank Norman Coton was appointed. Although there had been much change, the total complement of staff in 1989 remained at eight.

That year, at a departmental meeting the name of the Department was discussed – a meeting made livelier by a perceived unspoken agendum. The motion was to drop the Fluid Mechanics descriptor and simply use Aeronautics.. A counter proposal, to use Aerospace Science, was eventually replaced by Aerospace Engineering in the belief that it properly reflected the modern industry. So, the Department of Aeronautics and Fluid Mechanics became the Department of Aerospace Engineering.

It was also in 1989 that Professor Richards decided to demit office and was succeeded by Roderick Galbraith. On taking up his Headship he pursued two main objectives: research and teaching. Only essential administration would receive the same priority. Dr Galbraith felt there was no option but to adopt such a policy because of the severe workload that was extant on the staff, coupled to diminishing University resources.

The Consolidation

During 1991, after some lobbying outside the Faculty and considerable help from senior members of the University, a minor reshuffle was arranged and the Department welcomed three new academics to the Staff. Colin McInnes was a young and outstanding academic who specialised in Space-flight Dynamics and, in particular, solar sailing. He would become a world leader in solar sailing and have an extensive portfolio of research topics. Richard Gordon transferred from the Department's Research Technologist to a lectureship and, although he was research-inactive, made major contributions to teaching and to instilling a professional attitude in the students (he became the policeman of the Department). Stewart Houston, a product of

the Department and a helicopter flight-dynamicist returned to the Department after having spent time at the Royal Aerospace Establishment and a simulation company (VEGA). The final part of the reshuffle was to transfer Robert Gilmour from technician grade to Research Technologist, a move that benefited the Department richly, for Robert would go on to become a Wind Tunnel Instrumentation Specialist and help to bring the Department to world renown for its unsteady aerodynamics research. In 1991 also Roderick Galbraith and Roy Bradley were promoted: Roderick Galbraith to Reader and Roy Bradley to Senior Lecturer, shortly after which Roy left to become Head of Mathematics at another University.

In 1992 not only was Roderick Galbraith promoted to a Personal Chair in Aerodynamics, but also the Department was reaping the benefits of years of hard work. In 1993 Colin Goodchild was promoted to Senior Lecturer and in 1994, Roy Bradley's vacated post was filled by Dr Douglas Thomson. Douglas, another gifted product of the Department, would go on to develop the first successful helicopter inverse-flight-dynamics methodology, against which all others would be benchmarked. Also in that year a gentle-mannered stress analyst, David Coldbeck, graced the Department having spent many years in industry. In 1995/96 the Department was again pleased to welcome two new members of Staff, these being Dr Richard Green and Dr Ken Badcock.

This was also the centenary of the first UK controlled gliding flight by a Glasgow lecturer, Percy Pilcher, which had taken place at Cardross and, to celebrate the event, a commemorative lecture was given by Professor Roderick Galbraith and Professor Dugald Cameron (Director of the Glasgow School of Art). Over two hundred people attended, including the Principal (Sir Kerr Fraser) who, at the conclusion, accepted a commemorative painting of the historic flight, by Professor Cameron; it is hung in the visitors' centre for all to see. The lecture is now an annual event and has been given by some of our most outstanding graduates.

Sir Kerr Fraser accepting the Pilcher Painting from Professor Dugald Cameron and Professor Roderick Galbraith

Paul Tiasio Shoda, 1988 when he received his Honorary Degree

During 1996/97 Colin McInnes was promoted to a Readership and both Frank Coton and Ladislav Smrcek to Senior Lecturer. In 1997 the Shoda Chair (together with an annual lecture) was established and it is worth a minor digression here to elucidate some of its brief history.

The University of Glasgow has had a long association with Japan that started in 1873 when the University played a most important role in the establishment of the Imperial College of Engineering in Tokyo. A distinguished Glasgow Engineering Graduate, Dr Henry Dyer, became the College's first Principal; a post he held for nine years. This resulted in the establishment of the Imperial College by Henry Dyer and other Glasgow staff, initiating many Japanese students travelling to study at Glasgow. Among these was one Paul Tiasio Shoda who arrived in Glasgow in 1911 at the age of nineteen. He studied shipbuilding engineering at the University and graduated BSc in 1916 and thereafter became an apprentice at Dunmuir & Jackson for one year before returning to Japan and entering the Kobe Shipyard

of Mitsubishi. Later he manufactured the Japanese best able fighter, the Zero, and was involved in its mass production during the Second World War. He went on to a most distinguished career becoming Vice-President of Mitsubishi Industries. In 1988 he returned to Glasgow at the age of ninety-six to receive an Honorary degree of Doctor of Science.

At his request, fund-raising took place in Japan to establish the Shoda endowment for the purposes of funding a Chair in Aerospace Systems. Fund-raising in Japan was spearheaded by his son A Y Shoda and, in Scotland, by Professor Hugh Sutherland. In 1997 the Principal of the University of Glasgow, Sir Kerr Fraser, established the Chair and designated Professor Galbraith as the first holder. On his appointment Professor Galbraith felt very privileged and also grateful to both Al Shoda and Professor Sutherland.

Professor Galbraith was born in Lowmoor in 1947 and brought up in Greenock. The nature of the post-war town, and family circumstances, resulted in him attending four primary schools, a junior secondary and Greenock High School. He left school at sixteen to serve an apprenticeship in the local shipyard of Scott's and studied engineering at the James Watt Memorial College where he was awarded the Watt Medal. From there he spent six years at Paisley College of Technology (now Paisley University) gaining a BSc(Hons.) in mechanical engineering. The next three years were spent at Cambridge University reading aerodynamics towards a PhD with which he graduated in

Dr Arthur W Babister

HOT ROD

The student's caricature of Roderick Galbraith

Professor Colin McInnes

1976. In October 1975 he arrived at Glasgow for a one-year temporary appointment and has remained there. He and his co-workers constructed the Department's flow visualisation tunnels, established major dynamic-stall and blade-vortex interaction facilities that remain rare in the international community, They were awarded the Royal Aeronautical Society's Busk prize for their work on Dynamic Stall, published in 2001. Professor Galbraith was awarded a Doctor of the University of Paisley in 2001.

In his early bachelor years at Glasgow, Galbraith was renowned for his lack of sartorial elegance and, indeed, attended work one day wearing a red and a yellow sock together with a pair of shoes in which the worn out laces had been replaced by fuse wire. What the students thought of him is aptly illustrated by their caricature of him.

Returning to 1997, this was also the year when the project to transfer the BAE SYSTEMS' nine-foot by seven-foot wind tunnel from Hatfield to Glasgow was completed after a period of five years. To manage that facility, Dr David Hurst was appointed as a senior lecturer. The wind tunnel, the one in which all the early airbus wing-work was carried out, is a high-specification industrial-quality facility.

As was mentioned earlier Colin McInnes came to the Department as a young, very promising scholar and it was unsurprising that he was appointed to a Personal Chair of Space Systems in 1999.

Colin was born in Glasgow in 1969 and was educated at Knightswood Secondary School, coming to the University of Glasgow in 1984 to study in the Science Faculty. After obtaining a BSc (Hons) First Class in Physics and Astronomy in 1988, he was awarded a Robert Cormack Fellowship from the Royal Society of Edinburgh. The Cormack Fellowship was of great benefit to him, being one of the very few awards to a postgraduate student that permits personal research interests to be pursued with few preconditions. It was this freedom to pursue personal interests uninhibited that lead to the beginnings of his work on solar sail orbital dynamics, ultimately leading to the definitive research text on the subject some ten years later.

Following completion of his PhD, he was offered a lectureship at the Department of Aerospace Engineering with the remit to develop space-related teaching and research. New research interests, including spacecraft rendezvous and docking lead to contributions to the European involvement in the international space station programme. He was subsequently pro-

The wind tunnel in which all the early airbus wing-work was carried out
Professor Galbraith, Margaret McGarry, GDA and Trevor Truman, Engineering Director, BAE Systems, at it's opening

moted to Reader in 1996 and to a Personal Chair in Space Systems Engineering in 1999. His current, wide-ranging international activities in solar sailing, spacecraft autonomy and space robotics have been recognised through his election to Fellow of the Royal Aeronautical Society, Fellow of the Royal Society of Edinburgh and distinctions, such as the Royal Aeronautical Society Pardoe Space Award, the Royal Society of Edinburgh Bruce-Preller Prize Lectureship and a Leverhulme Trust Philip Leverhulme Prize. He collaborates widely, serving on the NASA Solar Sail Technology Working Group and acts as a consultant to several international space agencies and aerospace corporations.

Such was his devotion to the development of solar sailing that, in 1991, he flew to Moscow the day after the military coup which overthrew President Gorbachev, evading tanks and troops to take up a short-term post at the Russian Academy of Sciences. Never let it be said that academics only arrange

research visits to exotic locations with agreeable climates!

In 1991 also, Frank Coton was promoted to Reader and David Coldbeck returned to the aerospace industry. A serious gap appeared in the Department's teaching capabilities, in Flutter, caused by the departure of John Anderson. It was with relief that John's post was filled by Eric Gillies in the January of 1999.

In 2000, Ken Badcock was promoted to Senior Lecturer. David Pirie, who had taken early retirement in 1989 with part-time re-employment, retired fully and David Hurst left to take up a post with Jaguar Racing. The Department was also pleased to welcome Dr Chris York to a Senior Lectureship in Aircraft Structures.

In 2001 Marco Vezza was promoted to Senior Lecturer and Dr George Barakus was appointed to be a Lecturer in Computational Fluid Dynamics.

In 1998 the University adopted a new policy pertaining to

the tenure of Heads of Department. In essence, the Head of a Department could be appointed from any Senior Lecturer and above for a tenure of four years with a possible extension to six years. Hence, Professor Galbraith was disposed to comply and demitted office in October 2000; he was succeeded by Dr Douglas Thomson.

The Present

The Department's staff members comprise three professors, one reader, seven senior lecturers and three lecturers; in total fourteen. It has almost forty researchers and more than 330 students with a student staff ratio in the region of eighteen. The support staff number ten technicians, three secretaries and one administrator. For its excellence in research it was invited to become a founder member of two Defence Aerospace Partnerships; fully accredited by Foresight Committee. For its excellence in undergraduate teaching it is one of only three departments to have received 'Preferred Status' from BAE SYSTEMS. At the end of September 2000, the Department became 100% research active with just below 50% of the staff with recognised international reputations.

That international reputation is evidenced through the Department's consultancies and collaborations with, for example, NASA Ames, Jet Propulsion Laboratory, Lockheed Martin, BAE SYSTEMS, GKN Westlands, DERA (now QinetiQ), European Space Agency, Halcrow Crouch and the National Renewable Energy Laboratory of the United States. It participates in national, and international, committees and working groups and is fully involved in European Framework Programmes; it has sixteen European partners. It was one of the first Departments to introduce a European Master of Engineering and is the lead European Department for an International MSc/PhD Programme with the United States; soon to be extended to Canada and Brazil.

Wind tunnel experiment to help skiers achieve faster times

The current research portfolio:
Experimental Aerodynamics

Here, all the activity is associated with sub-sonic flow and, in particular, wind tunnel experiments. Over the past few years the Department has gained a truly international reputation for its work on nominally two and three-dimensional dynamic-stall and blade-vortex interaction. The former is associated with the performance of helicopter rotors and wind turbines, while the latter concerns the vibration and noise extant on all helicopters. The work was also developed into the performance of agile fighters and the airflow over their wings. The data acquired has been incorporated into the NATO data base for unsteady aerodynamics and the Department continues to maintain its international lead in its field. The instrumentation includes a 200 channel data acquisition system together with the latest velocity measuring systems. It has four tunnels capable of research work.

An interesting use of the facilities was assistance to the country's skiers and skeleton bobs to seek out the positions that give the lowest air resistance, hence the fastest times.

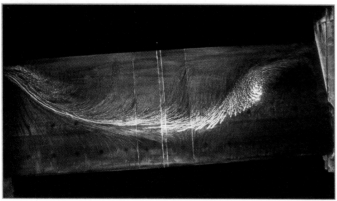

Wind tunnel experiments

Image of the simulation of the Papendorpse Bridge in the wind tunnel

Computer generated image of the predicted entire flow round an aircraft

Computational Fluid Dynamics

There are three aspects to the Departmental activities in Computational Fluid Dynamics (CFD). First, a commercial package has been adapted to be a part of the wind tunnel facilities. Here the CFD is complimentary to the experiments and assists in the interpretation of the measured data. It has been a most illuminating contribution to the experiments.

Second, a most delightful methodology, discrete vortex modelling, has been developed to consider both the flow over bluff bodies (bridges) and flow control over aerofoils. The computer code has been used by a major consultancy firm and is consequently marketed worldwide.

The last activity is the development of an in-house computer code to eventually tackle the 'Grand Challenge', which is the prediction of the entire flow around an aircraft. That code is currently used by major aerospace companies and contributes to European industry. It is a significant facility that can tackle very difficult problems such as flutter and hypersonic flow. The code is of international quality and has what is called a Parallel Multi-Block structure.

Computational fluid dynamics basically consists of a numerical analysis that divides the interested region of the chosen flow into very small packets whose dimensions are well defined: there can be many millions of these packets. The size and distribution of these packets (cells) varies across the flow field in blocks: hence the term 'Multi Block'.Such is the size of the

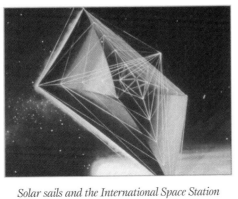

Solar sails and the International Space Station

resulting computation that it uses many computers simultaneously to obtain a result in a reasonable time.

In all computational fluid dynamics, however, the scientist is restricted by the lack of a closed form of equations, a consequence of turbulence which has yet to be adequately defined. To overcome the deficiency, scientists employ the closed form equations for laminar flow and simply adapt them for turbulent flow by decomposing the highly non-linear dependent variables into mean and fluctuating components. The equations are then time-averaged resulting in an indeterminate equation set. There are more unknowns than there are equations. At least one additional equation is required. While the programming and structure of the final code is sophisticated, the ingenuity of the additional equation dictates the final result.

Like the wind tunnel, it is the interpretation of the predictions that is the art of the engineer. Glasgow has been very productive in that regard.

Space-flight Dynamics

A range of Space Systems Engineering technologies are currently under development within the Department of Aerospace Engineering. Much of this work centres on advanced propulsion (solar sailing and, in collaboration with the Department of Mechanical Engineering, space tethers), which is complimented by studies on space robotics and spacecraft autonomy. Although some work represents fundamental research in Space Systems Engineering, much is mission-oriented and focused on future exploitation through international collaboration. In particular, early work on highly non-Keplerian orbits for solar sails has now been developed and is currently being exploited by NASA and ESA for mission studies on near-term uses of solar sail technology. For the longer term, the work at Glasgow could lay the foundations for towing masses, on an earthly collision course, into a near miss trajectory.

The work on potential field methods for spacecraft rendezvous and docking has been extended to multiple spacecraft applications and is being developed by ESA for use on a future optical interferometer mission requiring co-ordinated control of eight spacecraft.

Rotorcraft Flight Dynamics

All of the activities concerning flight dynamics are associated with rotorcraft. The Department are the world leaders in Inverse Simulation in which the pilot's response is predicted for

Helicopter safety procedures from off-shore oil platforms

a chosen manoeuvre. A most challenging task, and the associated methodology has been used to assist in the development of helicopter safety procedures from off-shore oil platforms, the procurement of the national defence helicopter, shipboard operations and in the certification of autogyros. The work became the benchmark against which all other codes were assessed.

The developed rotorcraft flight-dynamics work that considers the response of the rotorcraft to control inputs (ie pilot actions) is, like the inverse method, of international quality. The latest version has full rotor aerodynamic-modelling and its application has been both wide and varied. Of most significance, however, is the contribution it has made to the airworthiness of autogyros. This work became a major activity and laid down the foundations for autogyro certification.

Quite often it is difficult to obtain appropriate test data with which to validate the predictions. To this end the Department bought and then instrumented an autogyro. It remains the only such vehicle worldwide.

First all-metal powered glider to be
certified in the UK.
Managed by Glasgow and flown at
Oxford Air Training School

Unmanned
Air Performance Vehicle
used for aerofoil experiments

Design

These activities are concerned with aircraft performance, safety, and certification together with interests in fundamental structural behaviour. The latter particularly deals with structural instability and vibration response. The work therefore, forms a substantial interdisciplinary base for expansion into all aspects of aerospace design.

The areas in which a significant impact on aircraft safety design aspects have been achieved are: sail-planes/gliders and Unmanned Air Vehicles (UAVs) through the provision of data to the CAA (UK) and Joint Airworthiness Authority (JAA). A notable achievement was the UK certification of an all-metal motor glider from the (then) Eastern Block, the first in over fifty years.

The work continues and has led to the acquisition of an UAV, which is currently being modified to carry out in-flight experiments on novel and appropriate aerofoil designs.

Most practical applications and theoretical developments in design of airborne vehicles are within the Department's scope and benefit from the close industrial connections, both in the UK and abroad.

Air Traffic Management

The research interest in Avionics and Systems is concerned with the issues associated with Aircraft Operations and Communication, Navigation Surveillance/Air Traffic Management (CNS/ATM). The research encompasses the trend towards a macro concept of integrated avionics and offers a major challenge. That challenge is to produce a safety-critical, real-time system that integrates satellite, aircraft, computing and communications technologies, for the proposed Air Traffic Management (ATM).

The Department focuses on several aspects of CNS/ATM and works very closely with Euro control. The research has produced a simulation called Air Traffic Systems Simulated Environment Tool (ATSSET). It can consider aircraft operations including the integration of flight plan information, error and failure modes, air traffic conflicts, safety and risk analysis for high air-traffic density, variable and curved approach finals, and multiple runway operations.

The Future

The Department is vibrant and youthful and looks to the future with growing confidence. This is in spite of two decades of funding cuts and political meddling in the University sector. The particular 'Orwellian speak' adopted was that of 'Efficiency Gains' symbolising a cut. Over the past ten years the unit of resource to the Faculty of Engineering fell by 50%. Also, the period has been marked by a significant increase in the number of initiatives and reviews pursued in the name of 'transparency and accountability' for public funding. It is said that the only thing worse than a cut is yet another 'initiative' How then can it be anticipated that the high quality teaching and research will be sustained and indeed advanced? It is simply the high quality of the entire staff, – researchers, technicians, administrators and secretaries – a young and youthful staff, aware of their heritage, but with little of the baggage that comes with age and so no resistance to change. Survival is continual change and adaptation.

To the Department then and its future!

Two named, annual public lectures have been established by the University of Glasgow. These are the 'Pilcher' and 'Shoda' lecturer and are listed below. The Royal Aeronautical Society also has a number of 'named' lectures including the 'Barnwell' and the 'Stewart', both commemorating the life and works of these two Glasgow graduates and the 'McIntyre', appropriately at Prestwick.

The Pilcher Memorial Lecture 1995:

1995 Dugald Cameron & R Galbraith: Inaugural Lecture, *'One Hundred Years of Aviation in Scotland'*
1996 K McKay: *'Why it is as it is'*
1997 R McKinlay: *'Future Supersonic Aircraft'*
1998 P Wilby: *'Shock Waves In the Rotor World'*
1999 P Jarrett: *'Percy Pilcher and the Challenge of Flight'*
2000 Don Cameron: *'A Career in Ballooning'*
2001 Dugald Cameron & R Galbraith: *'Aerospace – the Gilmorehill Connection'*
2002 G Leishman: *'Technological Milestones in Early Helicopter Developments'*
2003 Bryan Richards: *'Simulating Aerodynamics–Making High Speed Flight Possible'*

The Shoda Lecture 1997:

1997 R Galbraith, Inaugural Lecture: *'Aerospace Systems'*
1998 J Farley: *'The Test Pilot's Job – A Personal View'*
1999 B Berry: *'Space Propulsion in Europe'*
2000 C McInnes: *'Desktop Space Exploration'*
2001 H McDonald: *'Aerospace Research in the Information Age'*
2002 Alan Simpson: *'The Tragedy of the R 101'*
2000 G Vette: *'The Erebus Disaster'*

A few graduate careers:

Director of NASA AMES
Chairman and Chief Executive of BAE Airbus
Managing Director of Eurofighter Systems
Technical Director of Westland Helicopters
Director of Engineering BAE
Chief Executive of Porthan
International Professors of Aerodynamics
and many more!

Acknowledgements

The information pertaining to the furth of Glasgow careers of Professors Duncan, Nonweiler and Richards was provided by the University archives with additions from Professor Simpson (Visiting Professor). They have been used verbatim, adapted and added to. The story of Duncan's fluids laboratory was taken from C Oakley's history of the Faculty. The background to the Shoda Chair has been taken or gleaned from the Department's Archive and in particular some written works of A Y Shoda and Professor Sutherland. Professor Colin McInnes provided the biographical information.

Roddy Galbraith, with the permission of those mentioned, has included the information without detailed reference to yield an uninterrupted short topical history. He is most grateful for all the help.

Roderick McD Galbraith 2003

CONCORDE, the epitome of the 'Art of Engineering'
The last visit to Glasgow 3 July 2000

Dr Douglas Thomson
Head of Department of Aerospace Engineering

THE DEPARTMENT is based in the James Watt Building overlooking Kelvingrove Park and at a research annexe off-campus in the West of Scotland Science Park. This annexe will be opened in late 2003 and will house the Department's two large research wind tunnels, flight vehicles and workshop. The Department has around 300 undergraduates studying for Bachelor of Engineering or Master of Engineering degrees in Aeronautical Engineering or Avionics, and around 30 postgraduate students studying for Master of Science or Doctor of Philosophy degrees. The Department is currently staffed by a group of fourteen highly motivated academics committed to achieve the highest quality both in their teaching and research. They are aided by a similar number of support staff: administrative, technical and computing.

Our undergraduate degree programmes remain the only ones in Scotland available to undergraduates seeking a professional education for a career in aerospace or avionics engineering. Our degrees are accredited with the Royal Aeronautical Society and our courses have preferred status with BAE SYSTEMS. The nature and content of our degrees equips our students with a wide range of abilities, in particular our graduates are endowed with a high level of numerate, analytical problem solving skills. Taking into account also the good reputation of our degrees, graduates are able to pursue careers in fields other than aerospace engineering. For example, recent graduates have found employment in such diverse industries as finance, law, IT, the armed forces and a range of other engineering and scientific disciplines. The degree programmes consist of a series of modules

Dr Douglas Thomson

covering the fundamentals of engineering, aeronautical engineering and engineering management, and a number of optional specialised modules. These specialised modules reflect the research expertise of the staff and include subjects such as helicopter dynamics, CFD, space flight dynamics and experimental aerodynamics.

Research interests are wide and varied covering a range of aerospace topics. Historically the Department's main research strength has been in aerodynamics and fluid mechanics, and this is still the case today. Currently there are two major research groups: Low Speed Aerodynamics and Computational Fluid Dynamics. The Low Speed Aerodynamics Group specialises in unsteady aerodynamic testing using the Department's wind tunnels. These include the 2.13m by 1.61m, 60m/s Handley Page tunnel and the 2.65m by 2.04m, 76m/s Hatfield tunnel both located in the Department's research annexe. There are a number of smaller tunnels, used mainly for undergraduate teaching and projects, located on the main campus. Notable among these is one brought back from Germany by Professor Duncan after the Second World War, and another in

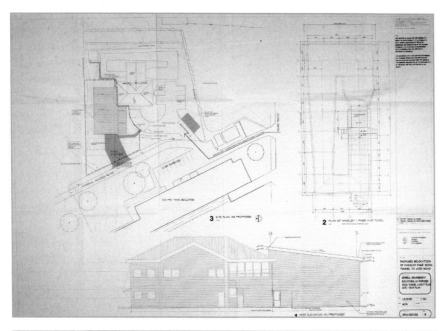

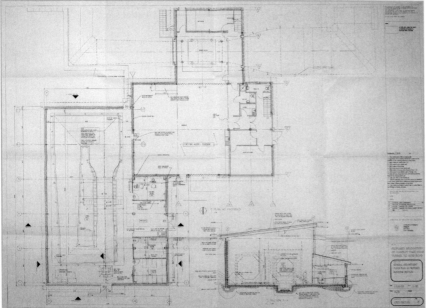

*Plan of Department of Aerospace Engineering
Research Annex to be commissioned Late 2003.
This annex houses the Hatfield (De Havilland) and
Handley Page low speed wind tunnels*

Sojka UAV
modified to carry Wing Glove
ready for launch

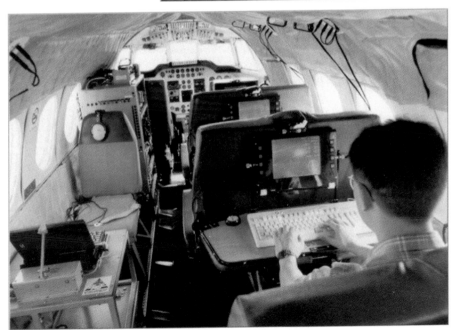

Master Students on flight testing course
on board the NFLC Cranfield Jetstream

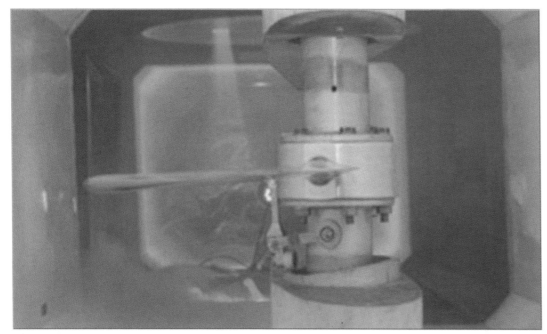

*Blade vortex
interaction experiment*

*Montgomerie-Parsons Autogyro
G-UNIV
embarking on a test flight*

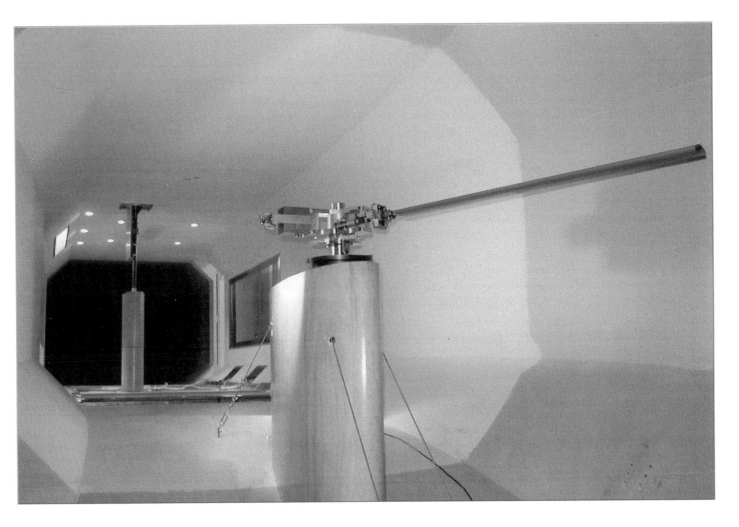

Rotor research in the Handley Page wind tunnel

the basement lab of the Anatomy building where Joseph Lister pioneered the work of antiseptic surgery. Major programmes involve ongoing research into flow control, blade vortex interaction and dynamic stall. The Computational Fluid Dynamics Group use state-of-the-art package, PMB developed in-house to solve a variety of complex flow problems including cavity flow prediction, non-linear flutter analysis, shock wave reflection, delta wing aerodynamics spiked body flows, engine surges and flow control using jets. The Department's Flight Dynamics Group specialises in research related to rotorcraft flight mechanics. The group has developed a range of rotorcraft mathematical models capable of simulating conventional helicopters, tilt-rotors and other novel configurations. The group operates a Montgomerie autogyro which was fully instrumented in-house to allow flight testing of the vehicle. The simulation models can be configured to simulate this autogyro aircraft which offers unique opportunities to develop model validation techniques and to study autorotative flight.

The Space Systems Engineering Group's main research theme is the development of autonomous, on-board systems for spacecraft with the aim of reducing their costs. One example of this was the development of an innovative new autonomous rendezvous and docking system for the European Space Agency. The Department has a world lead in the technologies associated with solar sailing. It also has a burgeoning Air Traffic Management and Avionics Group whose research is associated with aircraft operations, and Communication, Navigation Surveillance/Air Traffic Management. Finally, there is a Design and Structures Group whose research is concerned with aircraft performance, safety and certification together with fundamental structural behaviour, particularly with respect to instability and vibration response. One recent activity involved the modification of an Unmanned Air Vehicle (UAV) to carry out in-flight experiments of new aerofoil designs.

Each of the research groups is considered to be world-class in their achievements and research output. Currently we have research links with BAE SYSTEMS, Agusta-Westlands, the Civil Aviation Authority, Engineering and Physical Sciences Research Council, Medical Research Council, US Army, Lockheed Martin and Scottish Enterprise, and are involved in several European initiatives. All of our research activities feed into our undergraduate courses through course content and project work.

The UK is still a world leader in the aeronautical sciences, and the aerospace industry is the largest manufacturing sector in the UK economy. Within Scotland also there is a flourishing aerospace sector with Rolls-Royce, BAE SYSTEMS, and many other smaller supply chain companies based here. Rolls-Royce's new plant at Inchinnan, with an overall cost of £85 million is proof of their commitment to the West of Scotland. It will occupy a historic site near where Beardmore's assembled the R34 airship in 1919 and the buildings will be completed in 2003, the centenary of the Wright Brother's pioneering flights, with the final move from the 1939 plant at Hillington due in 2005.

The importance of a vibrant aeronautical engineering department within Scotland is quite clear. The support of Scottish and UK industry and the advancement of knowledge and understanding of aeronautics are at the heart of our mission statement:

The Department of Aerospace Engineering fully supports the University's mission statement of being research-led and operating in an international context. The Department's research profile clearly demonstrates compliance with this aim. The Department also aspires to possess 'well supported' academics capable of undertaking fundamental, strategic and applied research and also of providing education in the resulting research environment. Further, it is the aim of the Department to produce high quality graduates with appropriate skills and abilities for the UK aerospace industry. The Department also strives to direct its research into areas consistent with the interests of the UK industry and to fundamentally advance knowledge in aerospace engineering.

As the Department passes its 50th birthday and progresses into the 21st century it is reasonable to conclude that it has never been in better shape. Our high student numbers gives testament to the quality of our courses and of our teaching, while the support we receive from industry is evidence of research vitality. The Department can look optimistically towards the future continuing to produce graduates who will become the industry and research leaders of tomorrow.

THE DEPARTMENT OF AEROSPACE ENGINEERING

August 2003

Academic Staff

Dr D G Thomson	Head of Department
Professor F N Coton	Deputy Head of Department
Professor B E Richards	Mechan Chair, Chairman of Research Committee
Professor R A M Gaibraith	Shoda Chair
Professor C R McInnes	Personal Chair of Space Systems Engineering
Dr K Badcock	Reader
Dr G Barakos	Lecturer
Dr E A Gillies	Lecturer
Dr C Goodchild	Senior Lecturer
Dr R B Green	Senior Lecturer, Director of Undergraduate Teaching
Dr S Houston	Senior Lecturer
Mr G Radice	Lecturer
Dr L Smrcek	Senior Lecturer
Dr M Vezza	Senior Lecturer, Senior Adviser of Studies
Dr C York	Senior Lecturer
Professor H Wong	Emeritus Professor

Visiting Professors

Professor Dugald Cameron
Professor Alan Simpson

Administrative Staff

Miss C Pollock	Administrative Officer
Mrs H Boocock	Secretary to Head of Department
Ms A Queen	Departmental Secretary

Technical Staff

Mr R Gilmour	Research Technologist
Mr T Smedley	Chief Technician
J Carr	Technician
Ian Brown	Technician
Alexander Erwin	Technician
David Perrins	Technician
John Kitchin	Model Maker
Cameron Millar	Technician
Neil Owen	Technician
Ian Brown	Technician
Mrs L Floyd	Computing Assistant
Arran Fraser	Driver/Labourer

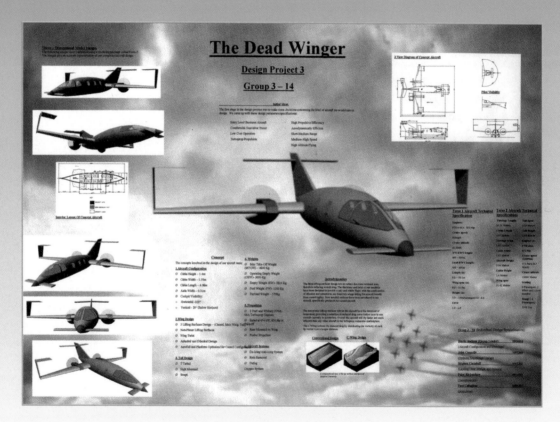

Winner of 3rd Year Group Design Project in 2003
(Barrie Andrew, John Connolly, Stephen Carnduff, Peter Richardson, Paul Callaghan)

FUTURE PROMISE

DURING the Centenary year of powered flight 2003 students at both the University of Glasgow, Department of Aerospace Engineering and the University of Strathclyde, Department of Design, Manufacture and Engineering Management faced up to the challenge of design for flight, part of the course for Gilmorehill a first for DMEM!

This account then closes witha a few illustrations of them and their work and a view of the Universities of Glasgow and Strathclyde Air Squadron whose four Grob 115e trainers now sport the 'Grey Douglas' tartan first worn by the pipe bands of both 602 (City of Glasgow) Squadron and 603 (City of Edinburgh) Squadron in the mid 1930s and later by the Vampires of 602 Squadron. A fitting commemoration of 602 whose post-war Spitfire F21, LA198 returned to the City's Museum of Transport in the Summer of 2003 to be eventually displayed in the refurbished Kelvingrove Museum and Art Gallery.

UGSAS won the old established 'Hack Trophy' and the

One of the four Grob 115E trainers of the Universities of Glasgow and Strathclyde sporting the 'Grey Douglas' tartan

The Universities of Glasgow and Strathclyde at their Easter Camp at RAF Kinloss, 2003

Richard Taylor explains the whys amd wherefores of a Bulldog to Strathclyde students

Miss Margaret Sinclair, Secretary to the Comanding Officer of the Universities of Glasgow and Strathclyde Air Squadron from 1941 to 1981

Acting Pilot Officer Katie Muldoon being presented the Rex Waite Trophy

newly established VT Trophy in 2003, commanded by Squadron Leader Andy Lawless, a Strathclyde graduate and former Squadron member.

The Squadron's- first secretary, Miss Margaret Sinclair, a remarkable lady, still takes a keen interest in 'her squadron', 62 years on!

Acting Pilot Officer Katie Muldoon received the Council of Military Education Committee's Prize of £500, for 2002/3. This is a UK award and is open to students in all three Service units, OTC, URNU and UAS. She also received the Rex Waite Trophy for the individual, section, flight or squadron making the greatest contribution to a charitable cause either financially or through humanitarian activities requiring imagination, determination and effort. She is seen here receiving that trophy from Sir Rex's son.

Katie studied aerospace engineering at the University of Glasgow. She was the Senior Student of the Universities of Glasgow and Strathclyde Air Squadron, 2002/3.

Among her achievements was to undertake an eight day sponsored cycle ride from St Petersburg to Moscow raising over £5,000 for SCOPE – a charity supporting research into cerebral palsy.

Katie is due to become an engineering officer in the Royal Air Force.

The future is going to be in good hands– here's to them!

'Team Jetstream'
University of Strathclyde
design students
who worked on the design
for an outward opening door
for the Jetstream 32
Robin Shuff, Marisa Smith,
Madelene McLeod and
Graham McGee

Eamon McHugh of Loganair tells it for real to
'Team Jetstream' students, March, 2003

Rory Partis makes his presentation

University of Glasgow Aerospace students
at the Museum of Flight, East Fortune

The final Jetstream 41s,
at British Aerospace, Prestwick 1997
The last complete commercially produced aircraft
to be designed and built in Scotland

The first aeroplane built in Glasgow by W & S Pollock, Robertson Street
(to enter for the flight from Glasgow to Edinburgh)

The PFA (Popular Flying Association)

Neil Geddes'
scale replica
of a SE5A

Its members are the real successors to those early pioneers for a 100 plus years on, they are hand building single and two seater light aircraft in their houses and garages. It may take years but eventually, the great satisfaction of flying what you made with your own hands, eyes and brain is a joy experienced.

Mike Timmins and his Rutan 'Long-eze'

The spirit of Kitty Hawk lives on

Martin Burns' Rutan 'Quickie'

Full circle! Return to Auchensail, David Wilson and Quentin Wilson with their replica 'Bat', 2001

INDEX

A recreation of Pllcher's powered triplane
built by Bill Brooks
flying successfully at Cranfield, September 2003